# BURNOUT RECOVERY

## 15 TECHNIQUES TO OVERCOME CHRONIC STRESS, REGAIN CONTROL, RESTORE YOUR ENERGY AND YOUR FOCUS

AMBER PIERCE

❀ Created with Vellum

# CONTENTS

# TWO SPECIAL GIFTS FOR OUR READERS

As a special thank you for getting this book, we would like to give you:

**6 TOOLS & EXERCISES TO OVERCOME STRESS**

Everything you need to help you manage stress in a healthy and effective way

+

**7-DAY CHALLENGE TO BURNOUT RECOVERY**

A step-by-step guide to kickstart you recovery journey

VISIT THEBURNOUTRECOVERYCLUB.COM/FREE-GIFTS | OR SCAN ME

**TO GET YOURS!**

# INTRODUCTION

You probably suspect that you are experiencing burnout or something that resembles burnout. This explains why you are holding this book. You are processing every word hoping to figure out a solution, to expel this sour feeling, to learn a better way to live. You say to yourself, 'This is no way to live!' You want a way out.

Before we go on, this is your cue to take slow, deep breaths. Close your eyes for five seconds and feel at ease in this moment. You are in the right place. Your suspicions are true; there is a better way to live and we will figure it out together.

With this, we begin our journey to discovery and self-restoration. The first thing to know is that anybody can experience burnout, irrespective of who you are or what you do. We often think about burnout on surface level. We try to sleep it off, wake up and go again, not realizing the cumulative effect burnout has on our body and quality of life. Here's the truth: Burnout is a big threat to your physical, mental, and social wellness. It is as serious as the most notorious health conditions you know. Yes, you heard right.

However, there is no need to fret. This book can educate and empower you on your journey to overcoming burnout. When I think back, I recall instances of my fingers going numb during my final hours of work. I recall the torturous journey home afterwards. There were nights I struggled to sleep because my mind was burdened with the thought of work, and there were days that I could barely keep my eyelids open at work. This is burnout; struggling between passing out and living for the same circumstance that triggers your burnout.

One day, my son threatened never to speak to me again. I was dumbfounded. He insisted that if I did not show up to cheer his soccer game, he would go cold towards me. I went to watch the game, though I had not been to his school for almost a year. I left a heap of files unattended at work and managed to show up at half-time, rushing in; you know that sprint-walk you do in an attempt to outrun time. I found myself wishing I could be two people at once in this universe. The most ridiculous thing was how I kept stealing time from this important moment of my son's life by going to the back of the crowd to receive lengthy work calls. I was as good as absent. But the good news is, my son did not end up ignoring my existence because well, he did sight me there after all, didn't he?

It suddenly occurred to me that I was sandwiched between too many things. I was burning out. Life was squeezing the juice out of me and I could no longer keep up. I was not suffering from kidney disease, cancer, or flu, which worsened my condition because I could not explain why I began to lag in everything. I struggled to be a good mom. I struggled with work. My life became brutally erroneous. Either the food got burnt in the kitchen or files got mixed up at the office. At this point, I stopped enjoying life. There was no room for growth or happiness. I was only taking up space and oxygen. I also said to myself, 'This is no way to live.' But what could I do differently?

Eventually, I admitted to myself that I would become everybody's fool if I continued down this path. I would never get a thumb up from my son, my husband or my superiors at work. I was patiently anticipating the day the HR Manager would invite me to his office and give me a piece of his mind. I was certain his patience was well stretched and tested and I could not blame him. I also ran out of patience with myself as I struggled to hold my life together to no avail. I felt pathetic.

I was driving home one midnight when all my stars aligned to send me a clue. I finally figured it out. I finally realized what hindered me from achieving my fullest potential. I held it right there, taking a closer look. It was my old friend burnout holding me hostage in a toxic association. I felt this brief rush of relief that comes with discovery, like I had been searching for water in a desert and finally found a bottle of water buried in the sand. A bottle of water, however, would only last a while. It was time to find the real deal—an actual solution.

You must know that if you have decided to tackle burnout, you have picked the proper battle. You have made the right enemy, and you must leave nothing to chance in this battle ring because burnout is a dreadful opponent.

You can learn how to subdue burnout, not just for now, but for the future, because it is not a once-in-a-lifetime thing. By learning the necessary skills required to deal with burnout, you will be empowered to deal with it at any point in your life. You will also be empowered to offer support to your family, friends and the people around you.

I had a firsthand experience of burnout while working as an accountant. I have also observed burnout among professionals in other disciplines, who often reach out to inquire about how best to handle it. Before writing this book, I used to write a few blog posts on stress and burnout. Subsequently, I began writing this book and the original idea was to create a short guide for my teammates and the people who approach me seeking knowledge on how to handle what they have erroneously termed "stress". I realized everyone could benefit from this knowledge, which motivated me to write for everyone who experiences symptoms of burnout.

In this book, you will learn that burnout is an epidemic. We will extensively define burnout, study its patterns, and discuss the implication of burnout for you. You will also learn practical ways to identify burnout as well as its various stages, empowering you to tailor the provided solutions to your burnout stage. In some chapters, exercises and ideas for journaling will be given, so I suggest you get a journal as soon as possible. The benefits of journaling are discussed in subsequent chapters, but for now, you should know that journaling serves as a tool to facilitate growth and wellbeing, as well as self-appreciation. Rereading old journals is also an effective way to discover how much you have evolved.

It is important for me to say that I am not a medical guru, nor do I have a magical anti-burnout recipe to make your burnout miraculously go away. What I am offering is a pool of experience gained from struggling with severe burnout for eighteen months. You will learn how to discover your burnout much earlier, how to find solutions that work for you and how to regain your balance. In the writing of this book, I consulted with counselors, health practitioners and psychologists, whose observations have hereby been documented. This book is a practical guide to answering every question you have about burnout and even questions you never knew you had.

There is so much for you to take from this book. All you have to do is flip through the pages and unravel knowledge that has the potential to change the trajectory of your life from a perpetual state of burnout to a state of wellness. I am beyond convinced that by the last page, you will have mastery of how to navigate your burnout journey. So, let us get started!

Best,

*Amber Pierce*

# CHAPTER 1
# THE BURNOUT EPIDEMIC

*It is health that is real wealth, and not pieces of gold and silver*

MAHATMA GANDHI

'Burnout' was first used in the United States in the 1970s and received no serious attention until it progressed to a notorious status in the 2000s. Since the term originated, it has been viewed as a bad omen associated with poorly managed lifestyle and inadequacy. A lot of us believe it is an extreme state of exhaustion during which the individual is running out of fuel and need to slow down.

Among many misconceptions about burnout, the old belief was that burnout occurred when the individual had physically and emotionally exhausted oneself while helping others, thought to be common only among professionals with caretaking responsibilities like healthcare, housekeeping, and teaching. Nobody suspected that an engineer or a farmer could experience burnout. The fact that people did not die of burnout also made it easier to ignore. What was the worst that could happen? Your mental, physical and emotional states are tossed about for a bit. Energy drains from your body. Work begins to feel too much of a chore and life becomes less colorful. So what? Life is yin and yang, push and pull, ups and downs. Hence, it was generally believed that as long as no death due to burnout was recorded, it did not deserve attention.

What remained uncovered was the dangerous truth behind the manifestation of burnout. We fail to identify burnout as a killer. A killer of dreams, self-esteem, happiness, relationships, and growth. It drags you into a bottomless bit and you do not realize when this dragging happens. You do not realize that you are in a chokehold.

Imagine a bucket sitting out in the rain. It is getting filled one drop at a time. You are staring at it from your window and it looks like it will never get filled, and even if it does, it would take forever. It looks like nothing is going on. But if the rain persists, that bucket will eventually get full. This scenario is similar to burnout. You do not see the damage, but it is there. And as long as the conditions triggering your burnout are unaddressed, little by little, burnout will continue its damage.

According to a 2019 journal by Stanford researchers, including Dr. Christine A and Shaha Hans, "burnout alone causes the United States an estimate of $5 billion annually, and it affects around 615 million people worldwide."

The World Health Organization (WHO) publicly announced that burnout is now among the global health conditions on their radar, saying, "Burnout is included in the 11$^{th}$ revision of the International Classification of Diseases (ICD-11) as an occupational phenomenon, not a medical condition." They further clarified that "occupational burnout is a syndrome resulting from chronic work-related stress, with symptoms characterized by feelings of energy depletion or exhaustion; increased mental distance from one's job, or feelings of negativism or cynicism related to one's job and reduced professional efficiency," with 120,000 annual deaths resulting from burnout-related conditions.

It is also important to add that burnout is not restricted to being an occupational phenomenon; it can occur in other aspects of our lives, such as parenting, marriage, and friendships. We can experience anxiety, overwhelming exhaustion, emotional numbness and lack of purpose for different reasons, with occupation being just one trigger. Therefore, I believe the term 'occupational burnout' is a subset of burnout as a whole and not an all-encompassing definition.

Emily Morse, an American sex therapist, author, and media personality writes about relationship burnout, stating that it "refers to two individuals in a romantic relationship gradually developing feelings of exhaustion, depression, and pessimism about their partner or dynamic," further explaining that "burnout can affect non-romantic relationships, including friendships, relationships with family members and loved ones, and coworker relationships." Dr. Puja Aggarwal, a board-certified neurologist and life coach, tells Healthline that "parental burnout is the physical, mental and emotional exhaustion that one feels from the chronic stress of parenting." He adds that "it can manifest with emotional distancing from your child or irritability. Some with parental burnout may experience forgetfulness and increased feelings of anxiety or depression, and many question their ability to be a parent in the first place. Feeling of inadequacy, confusion, and isolation are common."

These statistics and expanded definitions are necessary to haul burnout into the spotlight. Burnout is now recognized as an unusual disease with no known clinical remedy. You can take pills to treat its physical symptoms, which include headaches, nausea, digestive problems, weakened immunity, high blood pressure, and sleeping difficulties. But taking pills for these symptoms does not cater to the underlying psychological and emotional needs that must be met in treating burnout. It gets even more difficult with the WHO refusing to recommend or condemn any practical burnout remedy. This leaves us relying on therapeutic institutions, standard medical support, and recommendations from individuals who have survived burnout.

It gets increasingly terrifying when you realize how much the world has changed since burnout was first identified. The world's population grew a little over 5 billion in the nineties, with the United States' population being around 250 million. Nowadays, there are too many things demanding our very fickle attention, including social media, unscheduled meetings, ads, and traffic. Workspaces have become more competitive and hectic as organizations try to keep up with our fast-paced world. Inflation is on the high and the cost of living keeps skyrocketing. Every individual is striving to be relevant and different, to thrive amidst the noise and chaos. It is safe to say that whatever burnout was identified as back in the days was merely a preview.

Burnout has advanced. We are challenged with its premium version and none of us directly subscribed for this. We have dreams to fulfill, bills to pay, and while at it, we have to impress our bosses, our partners, our children, and extended relatives — we are even caught up with impressing our neighbors and at worst, total strangers. The pressure is insane, I know. Even children are burning out at an alarming rate. You may expect that the little ones have no worries in life, so learning that children experience burnout may sound a bit outlandish and ridiculous. But it is true.

There is the COVID-19 pandemic that snuck on humanity just when nobody was looking, bringing the world to a long standstill, a state of uncertainty, fear and disruption. The virus challenged everything we knew to be true and held dear. Our lives, our jobs, our families, our friendships and even our perspective of the future. The concept of tomorrow has become water cupped in our palms. Now you see it, the next moment it is gone.

The key to our survival was glaring: Adapt and find a new way to live or get lost in the turbulent wave of the virus. Business managers had trouble keeping their workplaces effective. Most businesses opted for remote operation, and workers agreed that it was not easy staying focused while working remotely. The rate of unemployment increased and stress levels broke the scale.

As reported by Mental Health America, the number of people looking for help with anxiety has plummeted following the COVID-19 outbreak, accompanied by an increase in depression and suicide. People are not just lonely; they are overworking as well. A lot of workplaces have updated demands, which require good adaptive skills and mental stamina. For example, professionals are now required to be tech-savvy, maintain enthusiasm while working remotely, and minimize distraction. In fact, it may seem like you need to be a superhuman to survive these times. Maybe have six arms for a start. At least you could hold your coffee, type a document, rock your child to sleep, flip the pancake on the fire and have two more arms to spare for unforeseen circumstances.

We have seen that burnout is not a little pebble on your path that you can underestimate or ignore. It is a monster—an epidemic. And if you do not take charge of your burnout condition today, it will only escalate.

In the next chapter, you will learn the substantive meaning of burnout and the conditions through which burnout disguises itself.

# CHAPTER 2
# AN ELABORATE VIEW INTO THE CONCEPT OF BURNOUT, SIMILAR CONDITIONS AND BURNOUT SYMPTOMS

---

*Burnout is nature's way of telling you; you've been going through the motions your soul has departed; you're a zombie, a member of the walking dead, a sleepwalker. False optimism is like administrating stimulants to an exhausted nervous system.*

SAM KEEN

---

If your job requires dealing with people on a regular basis, it can get overwhelming because you will meet all kinds of people while at it. You may encounter people with high emotional demands; those in need of help, love, and support. Adopting workable, efficient methods to meet the needs of these people will not be the easiest thing to do. You can get exhausted to a point where you are thrown off balance. A nurse may have to deal with emergencies requiring prompt action that triggers tension and stress. She might lose some the patients under her care. Therapists deal with several individuals going through hard times. A detective will sift through various criminal cases, of which there will be expectations to succeed.

Stealthily, these experiences nibble at the professional's

mental health and passion for the job until there is little to no enthusiasm left to support the execution of their duties. This leaves the professional feeling overburdened. They feel pressured, slowly detaching from the job as passion withers and morphs into dissatisfaction and disgust. From the outset, they knew what they signed up for. They just did not expect it to get this overwhelming or did not understand the full implication of the job.

In 1979, Herbert Freudenberger, an American psychologist, coined the term "burnout" to describe the sequel of these burdens on helping professionals. In the previous chapter, we realized this was merely a preview of burnout. The 21$^{st}$ century has exposed the extent to which burnout can manifest and wreak havoc. Living in commercial cities makes it even worse. Julia Fraga, San Francisco writer and psychologist, writes in a paper medically reviewed by Timothy J. Legg, PhD, PsyD, that "the hustle and bustle of urban life can take a big toll on your mental and physical health," further quoting a 2017 meta-analysis that found PTSD, anger management and generalized anxiety disorder to be prevalent among those living in urban areas. Forbes also listed top US cities in a research article titled *The World's 20 Most Stressed-Out Cities*, enlisting Los Angeles, Chicago, and New York, alongside other populous, urban cities like Mumbai (India), Sydney (Australia), Hanoi (Vietnam), Taipei (Taiwan), Buenos Aires (Argentina), and Seoul (Korea).

We must also consider the emergence of new industries and businesses. According to the American Progress Organization, over 3 million jobs were created across 30 emerging professional fields. Hence, people have become so immersed in career and engrossed with professional growth that they unknowingly begin to suffer the same symptoms the WHO officially identified among helping professionals who suffered burnout.

A 2019 study by the American Institute of Stress showed that only 6 percent of workers do not feel stressed at work. Similar surveys by the Wrike, Statista, Everest College and other institutions clarified that workload is the primary reason behind the stress of most employees. These employees believe their stress level affects their personal relationship, results in sleep deprivation, and sometimes trigger depression. The situation gradually evolves into what we regard as burnout.

Joe Robinson, an American health researcher, says "burnout occurs after a long period of chronic stress, during which all energetic resources—stress hormones, physical and mental vitality, positive emotions, willpower, resilience—and all other items in the coping reserves have been drained. We wind up fully depleted in a three-way shutdown: emotional exhaustion, physical fatigue, and cognitive weariness." You can feel inexplicably tired and be inefficient in carrying out your responsibilities. A mental distance can wedge between you and the job you once cherished so much. You may grunt when faced with the responsibilities you once took up with enthusiasm and always seek an escape from your job. This frustration and energy depletion characterize burnout.

It is important to know that burnout does not happen in isolation. Oftentimes, it is accompanied by notable symptoms, and experiencing one or two of these symptoms does not always indicate burnout. You must understand how to identify burnout to enable you combat it. If I had this knowledge, perhaps I would not have been engulfed by burnout for a good eighteen months of my life. It only became evident to me after series of consultations with counselors and psychiatrists who believed nothing was wrong with me. I was simply burning out without realizing it and without even knowing what it was.

Now, we will discuss the primary symptoms of burnout and how to differentiate it from other similar conditions.

## BURNOUT VS FATIGUE

Emotion is the clearest distinction between fatigue and burnout. After a long day, you may feel pains at your joints. You may feel tired, drained of strength and in need of uninterrupted sleep. This is a normal response that is independent of your emotions.

With burnout, there is little to no ecstasy, satisfaction, or positivity. In addition to physical fatigue, you will experience emotional and mental fatigue. You will find yourself always caught up in a race to the finish line. No passion, no zeal, you just want to be done. You are screaming internally and want to tear down everything that links you to that job you are growing to despise.

Typically, you can combat regular fatigue with exercise, a balanced diet, vitamins, sufficient rest, and maybe cutting down on caffeine if you are a coffee lover (or alcohol if you are a frequent consumer). I think of burnout and fatigue occurring through a process, the first and mildest stage being tiredness. Overeating or excessive laughter can make you tired, whereas stressful or overexerting activities result in fatigue.

Harvard Medical School professional, Jennifer Crystal, says, "Everyday fatigue that is not illness-related starts with a baseline of health. You may feel sleepy, you may in fact be sleep-deprived, or your body and mind may be worn out from long hours, exertion, or unrelenting stress—but you don't feel sick. Your muscles and joints don't ache like when you have the flu. You are capable of getting out of bed and powering through the day, even if you don't want to. A cup of coffee or a nap might perk you up."

During the manifestation of fatigue, your glands and organs function optimally. Your nervous system may be overworked, but it is not impaired. Burnout, however, does not afford you the luxury of wellbeing. It results from the accumulation of stress, fatigue, and tiredness, often progressing over a long period and exacerbating if left unaddressed.

Bear in mind that being lazy is significantly different from burnout. Laziness does not last long especially if you are an effective person by nature. Reviewing the stages of burnout will help you understand that there is a broad line between burnout and laziness.

## BURNOUT VS. STRESS

The National Library of Medicine describes stress as "a feeling of mental or emotional tension." When you are stressed, you experience more mental strain than usual. According to several health institutions like the Summa Health Organization, "Stress is not always bad. It is just our body's response to the new challenges we face all the time." The award-winning author of several stress management topics, Elizabeth Scott (Ph.D.), explains that "good stress also known as eustress happens when we feel genuinely excited about something." Your senses quicken. You experience hormonal surges and your pulses accelerate. You feel it when competing in a big game, going on a date, or working against a deadline. Good stress pushes you to surpass your limits, evolve, and grow. You feel stressed when your coach prompts you to increase your workout hours. When the bills come in, and you are not sure how to foot them.

"Usually, in response to acute stress, the body's sympathetic nervous system is activated by the sudden release of hormones," says medical doctor and editor, Steven Gans. "The sympathetic nervous system then stimulates the adrenal glands, triggering the release of catecholamines (including adrenaline and noradrenaline.) These hormones provide a surge of energy which makes you suddenly feel alive, agile, and ready to "fight" or 'flight.'"

It could be brief, requiring only a prompt response. For instance, you look up to find someone descending the staircase. This should not be a problem, except the person coming down the stairs is the last person you want to see. Here you are fidgeting and scrambling through your thoughts for an escape and dreading the possibility of interacting with them any second. Or you are at work gearing up for a presentation in the next five minutes but you cannot find one of your vital documents. Meanwhile, the biggest stakeholders and top executives of the company are behind the meeting door awaiting your arrival.

This brief stress described as "acute or short-term stress" is typically protective and inventive. It propels you to find creative solutions to deal with the current challenge in the most realistic way and subsides after the stressor is resolved. You probably find the missing document or realize that the person you are avoiding did not notice you.

Bad stress becomes "chronic stress" when it persists for a long time and thrives through habitual interactions that are potentially toxic. This could be a stressful work environment, a demanding partner, growing in an unsupportive household or being at a school where you are a victim of incessant bullying. Persistent chronic stress causes adverse effects to health and can precipitate symptoms such as insomnia, weight gain, anxiety, pain, headaches and high blood pressure.

In contrast to acute stress, chronic stress can aggravate your protective immune responses. Rather than become protective and progressive, your immune responses become sullen. Eventually, chronic stress amounts to burnout.

It may be difficult to distinguish burnout from stress, but they are not the same. In the case of burnout, you do not necessarily have to be under pressure or time constraint, but you will lack the enthusiasm to go about your usual activities. Craig Dike differentiates stress from burnout, suggesting that "with stress, there is an end in sight, but getting there may be difficult. Burnout on the other hand is a cycle of negative emotions and withdrawal that result from investing too much into something emotionally, intellectually, or physically without doing anything to restore yourself."

| Stress | Chronic exhaustion and bunout |
|---|---|
| Stress triggers extremely reactive emotions. | For burnout, your emotions need not be overly active. Rather, they are dampened. |
| Stress leads to anxiety disorders and physical breakdown. | Detachment and depression are the hallmarks of burnout, which explains why a person suffering from burnout will engage potentially harmful activities like substance abuse, social isolation, and self-criticism. |
| Stress is prevalent in urgent or emergency situations. | Situations of burnout are characterized by disinterest and hopelessness. |
| Stress is a mental or emotional state due to adverse conditions or tension. | Burnout is a condition that results from prolonged exposure to stress |
| Stress results in dissatisfaction with work. | Burnout results it boredom and cynicism towards work. |
| Stress involves struggling to cope with pressure and workload. | With burnout, you are exhausted and depleted of any hope or strength to attempt accomplishing tasks. |
| Stress comes and goes and can often be linked to an individual or situation. It is relatively easier to identify and resolve. | Burnout is harder to identify because it creeps into your life, progresses gradually and becomes the norm. Resolving burnout involves a long-term process. |
| When stressed, your identity is not altered. | Burnout results in loss of identity. You may feel like a shadow of your old self. |

## BURNOUT VS. DEPRESSION

It is especially difficult to distinguish burnout from depression because they both have similar patterns and effects. Burnout and depression can result in serious life impairments and have intersecting symptoms such as loss of interest, loss of appetite, and social withdrawal. However, the difference lies in the etiology (cause), duration, and management methods. While burnout is a result of prolonged, unresolved stress, depression does not always have a cause. It may be triggered by specific stress and may persist in the absence of stressors, whereas burnout can be resolved by addressing the causative stressors. Burnout can be improved by taking a break, doing more of what you love, setting boundaries, adopting mindfulness as a habit, social connection, and exercise, and is not often linked with suicidal attempts, unlike depression. It is important to note though, that you may experience burnout with or without depression, and untreated burnout may eventually lead to depression and anxiety.

## SYMPTOMS AND WARNING SIGNS OF BURNOUT

### 1. ANHEDONIA AND LOSS OF INTEREST

Loss of interest is the most evident sign of burnout and is easily detectable. As burnout progresses, you will no longer find fulfillment in things you used to love; at worst, they may even feel disgusting. Your workplace, the policies, the people, and your clients will lose their appeal. If you are a freelancer, you may start to envy those who dress up and drive to work every morning. The thought of sitting for hours and solving a new problem no longer triggers any excitement. For those who work nine to five, the morning thrill of driving to work and sliding into your office may wane without explanation. Reclining into this state of existence is the first sign that you are experiencing burnout. As my burnout condition progressed, I lost the spark and motivation I initially had for my job.

Its accomplice, Anhedonia, is a psychological condition that causes you to derive less satisfaction in the things that have always delighted you. It makes you hate not just the object but also its surrounding circumstances. If you derive less pleasure in your romantic relationship, you may begin to despise the bed you share, the business your partner does, or their favorite cologne. Likewise, you may start to resent your colleagues, superiors, or clients if your interest in your job is inexplicably dwindling. This hatred could be projected on your office desk, company brand or work laptop.

As a rule of thumb, anhedonia or a loss of interest can be triggered by many circumstances. You may not have a smooth relationship with your colleague, or you may have been assigned to something entirely out of your scope.

Anhedonia is resolved when the immediate causes are controlled. If you still feel a loss of interest despite curbing the immediate cause of a problem, the next most likely culprit is burnout.

## 2. CYNICISM

Cynicism is a mental attempt to disconnect yourself from something by building a negative or scornful attitude towards it. It is one of the most prominent symptoms of burnout. You may not kick off with this attitude at your workplace, but chronic stress may lead to cynicism. Usually, you feel bothered, overwhelmed, exhausted, and gradually become disinterested. As you become disinterested, you develop cynicism and begin to loathe the primary motivators that have kept you going. Cynicism manifests as blaming behavior, snarky comments, distant feelings, indifference towards work, pessimism, irritability, and mistrust. It can appear as bitterness directed towards colleagues, customers, patients or clients, and even most destructively, towards yourself.

## 3. THE FEELING OF INEFFICIENCY

Burnout can result in low productivity behaviors which in turn disrupt workflow. Economics defines inefficiency as a situation where scarce resources such as time and energy are not being put to best use.

The feeling of inefficiency can result from you not knowing your KPI (Key Performance Index) which helps you measure your progress in achieving your goals and your overall work efficiency.

Lack of communication, feedback, and support may also prevent you to meet up with your set standards. If you are experiencing burnout, you may miss deadlines on numerous occasions due to lack of motivation and focus.

According to the Social Market Foundation, happy employees tend to be up to 20 % more productive at work. On the contrary, inefficiency from people, processes, and equipments can cost companies up to 20–30 percent in annual revenue. It is, therefore, crucial businesses re-evaluate the importance of keeping their employees happy and content.

## 4. FATIGUE

Physical exhaustion is another indication of burnout. For me, it was the symptom that alerted me to the possibility of something being drastically wrong. My body would feel numb barely three hours into my arrival at work, and I would have headaches all the time. That kind of fatigue is not just about your work that day. It is an accumulative occurrence. It begins from the days you spend excessively long hours at work and worsens as you strain yourself to meet the tight schedules, inadvertently shortening your work breaks.

Like the other symptoms discussed, many conditions may trigger physical exhaustion (or something similar) including underactivity or overactivity. The saddest thing is that drugs do not profer a lasting remedy to the physical fatigue associated with burnout, they can only limit pain to a certain extent. Every day will seem like another day to drag yourself to work and feel bad for waking up to several more hours of soreness, cramps, pain, and discomforts. I have experienced this physical exhaustion several times in my life, often characterized by persistent pain. Constant aching throughout your body indicates physical exhaustion, which may be caused when you push your body to perform without allowing time for muscle recovery and repletion of energy supplies. If you notice a significant decline in energy levels, then you may be experiencing physical exhaustion. Your body's depleted energy reserves are causing you to feel tired, indicating a need to recover and refuel before being physically active again. As we progress on our journey to discovering the truths behind burnout, you will learn whether your physical fatigue is a direct consequence of burnout.

## 5. PSYCHOLOGICAL EXHAUSTION

Mental exhaustion is not as apparent as physical exhaustion, but this does not imply that it is less significant. In plain terms, psychological exhaustion refers to a situation in which your mind is overstressed and reluctant to concentrate on the current task. Crystal Pole, a renowned psychologist, holds the opinion that "psychological exhaustion can happen when your brain receives too much stimulation or has to maintain an intense level of activity without rest."

A common sign of psychological exhaustion is lacking excitement and energy to do the things you love—the things that would actually recharge your batteries. Perhaps, you are reluctant to hang out with friends, meet your partner, or be in a class.

I imagine psychological exhaustion as a faulty car engine. Outwardly, everything else might be in shape, but the driving force is not. No vehicle can function without its driving force. The human mind is our driving force, and our body is the vehicle.

## 6. LOSS OF CONCENTRATION

Firstly, I want to establish that losing interest is not the same as losing concentration, although they are interwoven. You are likely to lose concentration if you are no longer interested. A loss of concentration implies a cluttered mind. As a matter of fact, I struggled to concentrate on anything when I was burning out, whether or not I had lost interest in it.

There are many non-pathologic factors that can affect your

ability to concentrate, which may be positive or negative and totally independent of interest. A supervisor may be watching over your shoulder, leaving you edgy and cautious. Or you may have a date night fast approaching, and you cannot jolt out of the excitement. Your partner could be returning from a long trip or you may have just lost a good friend. In such situations, you can get over the loss of concentration after a few hours, days, or at maximum, weeks. When your loss of concentration is associated with burnout, it gets more complicated. You can't focus at all, even to complete the most mundane tasks.

## 7. CHRONIC STRESS

Chronic stress is a strong indicator of burnout. I was extremely stressed, to the point it dawned on me that I could be burning out. I knew I was overworking and going out of my way to keep up with my responsibilities. I had to cut my rest and stretch my work hours. Yet, I underperformed in all the tasks I was given. I thought I was not working hard enough, not realizing the problem was in fact overworking. I needed to do less.

Stress, like other symptoms, is not always a direct result of burnout. It generally occurs when you constantly have to physically or mentally exert yourself to meet demand. While stress is not exclusive to burnout, certain traits help you realize when your stress is solely due to your burnout. For instance, you may feel stressed while doing something you should not find so stressful or things that came to you naturally before. Going forward, you will learn that every individual has different stress points.

## 8. CHANGE IN APPETITE

Burnout is one of the many causes of appetite loss. In a 2015 American Psychological Association study, 39 percent of subjects admitted eating or overeating unhealthy foods in the previous month due to stress, while 31 percent said they skipped a meal because of stress. Some others experienced inconsistent appetite or hardly ate anything altogether. If you experience a loss of appetite with no improvement after a few weeks, watch out for other symptoms of burnout and take the burnout test to ascertain your burnout status.

## 9. PROCRASTINATION

Procrastination is another evidence of burnout. The truth is, anyone can choose to delay an activity. You can get out of bed late and show up to work late. You might stall your next project for whatever reason. However, if you are not the type to procrastinate and you suddenly find yourself doing it often, something is not right. Certain tasks begin to seem more insurmountable and complicated than they really are and may even bore you.

In a study by the StudyMode Student Psyche Report, 40 percent of students who experienced stress confirmed that they felt overwhelmed and were unsure of where to start, resulting in procrastination. Similarly, Jaffe, Stead, and Neufeld in a study have also linked procrastination to higher levels of stress and lower levels of wellbeing.

High levels of stress, as we now understand, are a primary cause of burnout. When a person procrastinates in such instances, they may have started to lose their self-esteem, confidence, and enthusiasm to carry out tasks.

People can procrastinate because they have lost a sense of purpose and direction. They may procrastinate when they feel anxious, lose concentration, develop unrealistic expectations (as perfectionists), or nurse negativity about their ability. They may even procrastinate as a coping mechanism to protect themselves because they are breaking under the weight of intense pressure and fear of failure.

Like the other symptoms, procrastination does not happen in isolation. As Jaffe and Stead observed, "Procrastination, avoidance, and rumination are all common symptoms of depression.

Depressed individuals may struggle to plan ahead, lose confidence in their ability, and adopt a 'what's the point' mentality. The treatment approach is known as behavioral activation, in which one schedules enjoyable activities that provide a sense of mastery or accomplishment, may help alleviate some of these effects."

## 10. DWINDLING QUALITY

Every role has a specific measurement for the quality of delivery. It could be the daily number of calls you make, the number of cold emails you converted, or the number of projects your team can successfully execute. When you start to experience burnout, your interest in your job will drastically decline, and the quality of your delivery will plunge. This could also be due to lack of motivation and diminished focus.

Consequently, you will realize that you deliver less than you used to. The praises stop coming in, and your confidence takes a nosedive. You may try to resuscitate your dying confidence, but you are already experiencing psychological exhaustion, so you only dribble around. Progress is stalled. This is especially true of people who measure their progress via metrics and impressions. A YouTuber or Social Media Manager burning out would cause a depreciation in their views, impressions, conversions, and success rates. Like a snowball effect, numbers get worse, the quality of the work worsens, and they begin to lose confidence and self-esteem.

When you experience two or more of the symptoms discussed above, you are most likely whether on the verge of burning out or already burning out. To know for sure, take the burnout test in chapter five.

So far, we have expanded our knowledge on burnout and distinguished it from similar conditions, going ahead to discuss the symptoms to look out for if you suspect that you are burning out.

## A WORD ON DRUG INTAKE

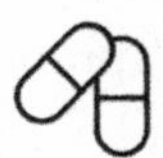

When I got invited to an open burnout session by Dr. Bernett for the first time, the first lesson revolved around drug use. According to the participant who spoke, resorting to drugs is one of the most common ways people cope with burnout. The National Institute on Drug Abuse says "brain research now indicates that people exposed to stress are more likely to abuse alcohol or other drugs, or to relapse to drug addiction." This is especially true of people who experience physical symptoms while burning out as well as people who are overwhelmed, anxious, and struggling with insomnia.

You may feel frustrated and directionless so you start to constantly rely on drugs and stimulants to achieve temporary relief from your health conditions. Some use pain relievers while others become addicted to stimulants like nicotine or alcohol.

Although drugs can be helpful and necessary in some cases, I think learning to live without them is vital, as they can end up making your unfocused brain even foggier or making you dependent.

# CHAPTER 3
# BURNOUT STAGES AND CATEGORIES

*The No. 1 cause of burnout is doing the same thing repeatedly and not seeing results.*

STEVE KACZMARSKI

We now understand that burnout is a peculiar health condition distinct from fatigue and stress, characterized by persistent emotional exhaustion, lack of enthusiasm and a general feeling of unwellness. Despite these warning signs, most people never realize they are burning out before it is too late. To help you understand the pathophysiology of burnout, we will now discuss the different categories and stages of burnouts.

## THE STAGES OF BURNOUT

### STAGE 1: THE HONEYMOON

The honeymoon stage is considered the beginner stage where the path to burnout is kindled. Some psychologists believe that the honeymoon stage should not be listed among the fundamental stages of burnout because people exhibit no signs of burnout. The more acceptable school of thought holds that the honeymoon stage is the foundation on which burnout is initiated and escalates. It is therefore important to acknowledge its role in the progression of burnout.

In the honeymoon phase, you find yourself in a new situation you have always wanted, which could be a new job, welcoming a child, or getting married. It is normal to be enthusiastic and excited at this point. You are bubbling with delight despite recognizing the bulk of effort required to make the situation work because you are willing to pull through with it. At your workplace, you are bristling with energy and a determination to prove your worth. You diligently tackle the responsibilities that come your way, oftentimes without giving yourself a breather.

Similarly, getting into a new relationship or having a baby may be a remarkable life experience for you. You have someone you are happy to go miles for and you are willing to compromise to make it work. You will have no trouble committing your time, money, and energy to the relationship. It will feel like a honeymoon.

There are no signs of negativism or burnout at this point. You may occasionally experience tiredness, stress, and fatigue, but these do not strike you as a big deal or a cause for concern. However, the overwhelming responsibilities accompanying these situations can potentiate the next stage of burnout—the onset of stress.

## STAGE 2: THE ONSET OF STRESS

This phase is where stress as a detrimental phenomenon becomes apparent. The honeymoon thrill begins to fade, fatigue creeps in, and your productivity takes a nosedive. It is easier to notice when you work in a highly demanding environment. You neglect your personal needs and notice changes in your appetite. You no longer have time for your weekend routines, cannot make time to walk your dog, or help your child with homework. It feels like there is always something more important to do and time becomes your greatest enemy as you are constantly running against it. With the onset of fatigue, sleep eludes you and leisure activities will feel like a burden.

You will occasionally experience headaches and palpitations. You will lose touch with your friends and family, and it will irritate and frustrate you, but you won't acknowledge it because you still do not see the problem. You brush past the feeling and distract yourself with work. You feel like whatever you are going through is normal—a price to pay for the opportunity you have been given. Your job stealthily becomes your priority while everything else fades. Even your partner you reverently adored now seems to be invading your personal space and clogging your thoughts in a way you may find slightly annoying. This is the point where you can nip your burnout in the bud. If you are unable to manage your stressors at this point, it upscales to chronic stress.

## STAGE 3: CHRONIC STRESS

In the previous chapter, we discussed good stress (eustress), a beneficial stress that has positive effect on health and wellbeing, alongside its counterpart, bad stress , that results in breakdown, mental and physical illness, and burnout. Chronic stress—which is bad stress—is characterized by prolonged, unresolved stress and is consequential to poor management of the previous stage. Between spending long hours at work and showing up for night classes, you can hardly find time to rest or evaluate your mental and emotional health. You neglect your mental and physical fatigue, leaving room for them to develop into chronic stress. In the event of chronic stress, you are dismantled from the inside while struggling to hold it all together, but there are too many things to grasp that they fall through the spaces between your fingers. You feel sandwiched between physical stress, lack of direction, and the feeling of being misunderstood. Your constant worry wears down your body, leaving you tired and anxious.

Everyone is overly demanding; at least that is what you think. Your boss suggesting you did not carry out a thorough job on your assigned task, your partner complaining about your lack of attention, your child sulking at a corner about something you failed to do, and there you are, feeling like being one person is not enough and you need to exist in multiple places at the same time—feeling like nobody is acknowledging your effort because if you are not doing enough, then why do you feel so worn out? It can be very frustrating to cope at this point.

You may feel like you never get a break at work and are under intense pressure to perform. You wake every morning unwilling to face the day's struggles, dragging through your activities and missing work deadlines, and may even develop aggressive behavior towards your co-workers, which may extend to your friends and family. There is pent-up anger brewing in you, awaiting its next victim. It should be no surprise that you are triggered by the littlest thing that would ordinarily be overlookable.

Low sex drive is also one of the many undetectable problems associated with chronic stress. The idea of sex may become largely uninviting—generally, you will lose interest in a lot of things, just as I realized I had lost interest in everything. It got complicated as problems in one aspect of my life rolled over to another aspect. Difficulty at home meant difficulty at work. Poor relationship with my husband translated to poor relationship with my friends. Trouble at work fostered unwillingness to engage in any leisure activity.

The advancement of chronic stress results in denial. You are exhausted, lacking enthusiasm and losing control, but you do not want to admit it. You convince yourself that you are still in control and struggle to stay relevant. You may even adopt unhealthy behaviors in a desperate ploy to feel in control—like spending longer hours on social media, caffeine consumption to keep up at work, or higher-than-average drug or alcohol intake. Whether your burnout originates from excessively long hours at work, relationship or parenting, you will realize something is wrong, which may cause you to panic.

## IDENTIFYING CHRONIC STRESS

Chronic stress is pervasive and long-lasting, so people often grow accustomed to it, even to the point that it becomes a norm. This may increase the difficulty of identifying chronic stress in your life. In the event of chronic stress, you are at risk of burning out and must take action before it escalates. Here are some signs of chronic stress to look for:

- Frequent moodiness or irritation
- Persistent anxiety
- Reliance on unhealthy coping mechanisms to manage stress
- Inability to make time for the things you enjoy and the people you care about
- Being inconvenienced by little tasks
- Frequent colds and infections

## STAGE 4: BURNOUT

Here you are in a state of full-fledged burnout. This is your limit and you can probably feel yourself ready to implode with overwhelm. You will experience aggravated physical symptoms including chronic headaches, general body pains, and digestive problems. You show up to work every morning with a feeling of emptiness especially if you have worked the same job for several years. No thrill. No creativity. You may even want to stay away from friends who seem to progress in their careers. Your self-confidence is tossed into a bottomless pit and all you are left with is self-doubt and anxiety.

It is important to know that you may not exhibit all these symptoms. You have to pay close attention to realize the onset of anomaly. Oblivion explains why many people may not recognize stage II until it progresses to stage III. When this happens, you may not be able to help yourself since you do not know the gravity of the situation or how best to deal with it. The self-help steps in chapter five will help you identify the exact stage of your burnout and what steps to take from there to regain happiness and inner balance.

## STAGE 5: HABITUAL BURNOUT

At this point, burnout becomes a default in your life. It is the only way you know to live. Chronic pain, alongside physical and mental fatigue, disrupts your ability to function properly. You are unable to concentrate and cannot complete the simplest tasks at home and at work; and your mind feels foggy. Every day feels like a bad day, nothing seems to play out to your advantage, your life loses its colors, and nothing makes sense anymore. Burnout at this stage can persist for a very long time and it may not be obvious to you or to those around you that you are, in fact, burning out. Your colleagues, friends, and family that are particularly attentive may notice something is wrong but not identify it as burnout. You may notice that you are almost always unhappy, and not being able to identify the cause or overcome the feeling may cause you to feel worse.

In addition to the five stages we have discussed, Herbert Freudenberger and Gail North outline the pathophysiology of burnout in these 12 stages:

1. Excessive drive/ambition
2. Pushing yourself to work harder
3. Neglecting your own needs
4. Displacement of conflict (Blaming external factors for your shortcomings)
5. No time for non-work-related needs
6. Denial (You are still convinced you are not the problem. In fact, you think there is no problem at all)
7. Withdrawal (You believe nobody understands you and severe connection with friends and family)
8. Behavioral changes
9. Depersonalization
10. Inner emptiness or anxiety
11. Depression
12. Mental or physical collapse

I expect that you assess yourself with the stages we have discussed and ascertain exactly where you belong. At this juncture, we will look into the categories of burnout.

---

Researchers have concluded that there are three types of burnout. They are:

## A. OVERLOAD BURNOUT

Overload burnout emanates from pressure and overworking. You get into a workplace, enjoy the environment, and creatively take on the challenge until it becomes toxic and overwhelming. In essence, your burnout is based on having too many demands and expectations to fulfill. You struggle to resist the pressure while trying to balance your professional and personal life. This type of burnout is also known as burnout by volume.

## B. UNDER-CHALLENGED BURNOUT

You may also slip into burnout due to boredom and underactivity, or due to the overly repetitive nature of your tasks. It is a common problem for overachievers and perfectionists. Unlike the typical honeymoon phase where you have too many activities, you may have too little to do. You may have high expectations for your job/relationship, anticipating a lot of excitement. You may be stoked to finally be able to apply your skills in an environment where they are relevant. Sadly, the job presented to you provides a challenge too insignificant for your expectations. Whether it be because you were disappointed from the start, but you assumed it would get better over the years, so you stuck around, or because you got bored of doing the exact same thing over the years, the result is the same. The situation does not improve and you end up feeling unmotivated, unfulfilled, fatigued, and utterly disinterested in work. You realize that your job is an unfulfilling venture and fatigue sets in.

Lack of autonomy at your workplace may also result in under-challenge burnout. Autonomy here implies having a sense of independence and being trusted to accomplish tasks for which your skills are suited. This will enable you to scale up as you are constantly faced with new challenges that stimulate your imagination. If as a writer in a literary magazine, you are only allowed to organize documents and upload articles to the company website, you will constantly feel that your skills are underutilized, which will cause a recline into a bore-out phase, subsequently leading to mental and physical dissatisfaction, and finally burnout.

## C. NEGLECT BURNOUT

Neglect burnout happens when your burnout has nothing to do with the bulkiness of your tasks or how challenging it appears. In essence, you are not under-challenged or over-saddled. You are just not in synchrony with the job or relationship.

Let us assume you start a job at a security firm, which requires you to stand at the same spot all day. You can tell from the start that you do not find the job exciting. Nonetheless, your enthusiasm to foot your bills keeps you going, so you do not overthink the neutrality you are feeling. The problem sets in when footing the bills becomes less of a motivation to continue your job as time passes. Everything about this security job now irks you. The work policies, your uniform—even the frequent client that always greets you when they drop by. You develop fatigue and disinterest and may begin to contribute less effort. Despite not being thrilled about the job, quitting sounds like a terrible idea. Instead, you struggle to revive the energy and enthusiasm with which you started.

The security job is merely an illustration. You can experience neglect burnout anywhere you work. The important thing to note is that neglect burnout occurs when your job does not enthuse you or spark much interest.

Now that we understand the stages and the types of burnout, it is important to inquire about its cause. Why does it happen? Burnouts are like burst pipes. Everything in you drains through the leakage and you cannot fix the pipe if you do not have precise knowledge of what burst the pipe, why it got burst, and how to prevent a recurrence of this incident. The next chapter will discuss the possible causes of burnout and practical combative solutions.

# CHAPTER 4
# THE ACTUAL REASON YOU ARE BURNING OUT

*Burnout is often driven by the demands that are placed upon an individual*

ASA DON BROWN

The previous chapter makes it clear that burnout does not happen overnight. It is a result of detrimental actions that have remained unresolved for an extensive period and accumulated to the point where you can no longer lead a normal, fulfilling life. It follows a parasitic pattern, ravaging its host until there is nothing left to ruin.

We must backtrack to observe the actions and inactions that may trigger the development of burnout if any tangible solution is to be established. As with any initiative geared towards resolving a problem, we must understand the 'why' to allow other relevant conversations to reveal themselves in the process, and thus unravel how to deal with the problem. Understanding the causes of burnout takes us to the very heart of the condition from where it can be dismantled inside out.

In this chapter, we will discuss the common causes of burnout after which you can use this knowledge to assess yourself and determine how you can detach from situations that place you on a path inevitably leading to burnout.

## SOME COMMON CAUSES OF BURNOUT

### 1. WORKLOAD/PRESSURE

A 2018 study by Peter Smith and some other colleagues at the BMC Public Health, reported that "high demands are associated with greater risk of burnout, regardless of the level of other work supports." In plainer terms, no matter how much support you have, you are likely to burn out when you have a lot of tasks to handle. It gets worse if these high demands are not supplemented with ample resources. When you work in an environment where you constantly overexert yourself, you will burn out in no time.

From a personal standpoint, I can tell you that burnout is inevitable if your success is measured by how hard you work. You are likely to experience burnout if you have to steal some time away to snack because lunch is a luxury at your workplace, or you always return home with a large heap of files despite reporting to work early every day, and late every night. This pressure extends to other aspects of your life including your relationship with your friends, partner, children and other people around you.

### 2. ENDURANCE

Endurance is another factor that is critical to the emergence of burnout. In chapter six, you will learn that every individual has a unique breaking point. What you and I can endure as separate entities differs significantly. The implication is that if I have a low breaking point, I will easily succumb to the weight of intense pressure, leaving me exposed to mental and physical stress. This sequentially advances to chronic stress and burnout.

In addition to endurance, mindset plays a key role. You may experience burnout because you are not psychologically inclined to do the job. You feel pessimistic, neutral, or unfulfilled. You are not motivated to work and your body will respond to this signal. A positive mindset offers more resistance to the encroachment of burnout. You are more motivated, you try to see the bright side to even the worst situations, you put your best foot forwards and are less prone to giving up when challenged by a roadblock. When you generate positive thoughts, your body produces serotonin (happy hormone) and decreases cortisol (stress hormone), facilitating a general feeling of wellbeing. Normal serotonin levels induce calmness, happiness, reduced anxiety, focus, and improved emotional stability. This would in turn improve your endurance. I will explain a negative mindset as losing the race before it even starts because there is no willpower driving you to the finish line. With a negative mindset, a lot of things will seem impossible and whatever joy you can notice in your work, relationship and personal life will be suffocated.

## 3. PERCEIVED LACK OF CONTROL

This is liable to occur in workplaces that adopt the top-down communication system. The directors make all the decisions, and pass the directives down the ladder until it reaches your level of operation. At this point, you have to do what is required, even if it is against what you think is ideal, irrelevant, or does not align with the workplace policies. You only execute the task out of obligation, which leaves you feeling like you are not contributing to anything, especially if you answer to superiors that are not open to employee suggestions. Nobody will be happy to arrive at work every day and engage in activities that seem insignificant. When this happens for an extended period, you will develop mental fatigue and disinterest in your job and you know what comes knocking afterwards —burnout.

## 4. YOUR ENVIRONMENT

A lot of our actions (or inactions) and decision-making processes are conditioned or influenced by our environment. While it is ideal to stay in control of your emotions, you are likely to be influenced by the circumstances surrounding you. If you work in a toxic environment, you will find yourself accepting things beyond your limits and to the detriment of your health. You will be suffocated by unempathetic, uninspiring, and uncreative colleagues or superiors.

## 5. VALUES MISMATCH

You may find yourself in situations where you do not uphold the same beliefs as your partner or your superior at work. If you consider fluid communication important, but you work with someone that makes all the decisions without carrying employees along, or someone that is not intentional about respecting your ideas and innovations, you may feel under-appreciated and misunderstood. Jackson Hogg, a leading recruiter in Newcastle, England, says, "It comes as no surprise that people look for other opportunities when faced with spending 40 hours per week with people they don't get on with." Christina Maslach adds that "when there is a values conflict on the job, and thus a gap between individual and organizational values, employees will find themselves making a trade-off between work they want to do and work they have to do, and this can lead to greater burnout." To further emphasize the importance of value alignment, Anne McKee in her book *How to Be Happy at Work* says, "When work is an expression of our values and we have a positive impact on something we care about, we are motivated from within." A mismatch of values can lead to poor cooperation, unhappiness, and frustration.

Now that you know the possible reasons why you are burning out, we will discuss self-diagnostic tools that can provide great assistance in your burnout recovery journey.

# CHAPTER 5
# BURNOUT EVALUATION TEST

The answer to whether you are burning out or not is not quite straightforward. There are questions you must ask yourself to evaluate your burnout status. These questions will help you assess your psychological condition, identify how you feel and assist you in finding missing pieces of the puzzle. Beyond being identifiers for burnout, these questions will also help you determine the exact stage of your burnout.

I coined these questions after my counselor confirmed I was burning out. In addition, I attended several sessions that empowered me with the knowledge to distinguish the different stages of burnout. You should know that I have suggested this test to many of my friends who were experiencing burnout, and it has indeed been very helpful and pivotal in their steps to recovery. In chapter two, I listed out some symptoms to look out for at every stage of a typical burnout occurrence. If you are yet to identify them, the subsequent self-assessment questions and diagnostic tools will guide you toward clarity.

Note that being completely honest and transparent while answering these questions will enable you to obtain the best results. To give this process an improved sense of direction and guide your thoughts, the questions presented are work-related, but can also be applied to other aspects of your life (family, parenting, and relationships). Let us dig in right away!

## BURNOUT QUIZ QUESTIONS

### STAGE 1: THE HONEYMOON PHASE

1. Am I unusually excited to get started with my new job or undertake new work tasks?
2. Does work make me feel enthusiastic and highly committed?
3. Do I feel like the demands of my job inhibit my regular life?
4. Is tiredness/fatigue/boredom frequent in my life? If yes, do I often ignore the feeling or leave them unaddressed?
5. Are you constantly overstretching your skills to fit the requirement of certain projects and opportunities at all costs?
6. Does my work feel like a honeymoon (following the reading of chapter 4)?

If you answered yes to three or more of the five questions above, you are in the honeymoon phase of burnout. You need to be more cautious, especially to prevent overworking, as it can induce stress and edge you to the next stage without you realizing it. It can also be useful to write down the things you cherish most about your job/relationship, in a place that is easily accessible, at this stage. This will keep you grounded especially when lack of enthusiasm or difficulty make these things less visible. Constantly telling yourself what you love about something reduces the chances of emotional disconnection. More about this will be discussed in chapter eight.

You are more likely to have a result indicating potential burnout in the next level of self-assessment if your answers in this stage are mostly positive because it means you are in the honeymoon stage and may already be treading down the path to onset stress. If your answers are neutral, you are less likely to experience burnout. If your answers are negative because you have gone beyond the honeymoon stage, you may experience some symptoms discussed in the next stage below.

## STAGE 2: THE ONSET OF STRESS

1. Do I feel like I do not like my job as much as I used to?
2. Do I sympathize less with my clients/company's needs?
3. Has there been a decline in my enthusiasm since I started?
4. Have I started to nurse negative thoughts about my job?
5. Am I beginning to doubt my ability to cope?
6. Do I have unspoken problems, especially in my job/co-workers?
7. Do I feel understood and supported by my superiors and/or colleagues?
8. Do I feel like my opinion is not valued?
9. Am I getting irritated by minor problems?
10. Do I feel like I have no one to talk to and confide in?
11. Does it seem like I am exchanging my old routines and leisure time with unhealthy habits and new activities that are not as fulfilling?
12. Am I feeling anxious?
13. Are there tasks that I keep procrastinating?
14. Am I having a hard time getting up in the morning?

Some assessment questions in the onset of stress stage may require you to provide more than a yes or no response. If about half or more of your answers tilt towards the positive side, there is every chance that you are on the path to burnout, and you must return to the drawing board as soon as possible.

In my case, I could not return to the drawing board because I did not realize my burnout until it was too intense. You have to stop, take a breath and take stock of the situation. And that's what I invite you to do today. You need to reflect on why you chose this job or relationship (or whatever situation) in the first place. Why were you drawn to it? Consciously begin to pinpoint aspects that may be toxic and unbearable as well. Afterward, see if you can change them or change your approach toward them. This will be elaborated in subsequent chapters.

As part of this assessment, I want you to carry out this exercise:

**Write down three major aspects of your life that are causing you stress. Be very specific about this procedure. For each enlisted item, write what factors are within your control and what you could do to manage the situation. Finally, reflect on what you could change to feel less stressed.**

## STAGE 3: CHRONIC STRESS

1. Are there problems that have persistently bothered me since I took up this job?
2. Are there things I hate about my job that happen too frequently?
3. Am I beginning to resent my job or partner? Am I avoiding calls/texts/meet-ups?
4. Do I feel bored, anxious, uninspired, and frustrated when I think about work in the morning?
5. Am I losing focus and concentration?
6. Do I become aggressive or moody when asked about my job/relationship?
7. Do I feel like I belong here or will staying here cost my sanity?

8. Do I always feel tired, exhausted, or generally weak?
9. Am I becoming less interested in social interactions?
10. Do I find the thought of sex uninteresting or am I not even thinking about it?
11. Am I adopting coping mechanisms to shield me from tackling a certain problem?
12. Do I struggle with my work-personal life balance?
13. Do I no longer have time for my passions, hobbies, and other activities because of my job?
14. Do I constantly think about work outside of my office hours and do I think about my personal problems at work?
15. Do I frequently fall behind schedule to the point that my supervisor knows me for delay and poor delivery?
16. Do I feel like I am never organized enough to accomplish all the tasks at hand?
17. Do I honestly think this job is right for me as it is right now?
18. Does it seem like my current job's values are pulling me apart from the life I would like to have?

The bulk of questions for this phase are close-ended; a simple yes or no may suffice and you can navigate through them quickly. However, still take your time and give it deep thought before you provide a response. You are in the chronic stress stage if up to half of your answers are in the affirmative. If you have three to five positive answers, you are sandwiched between the honeymoon phase and the onset of stress.

## STAGE 4: BURNOUT

1. Do I feel exhausted every time I think about my job?
2. Do I feel like I am living through toxic circumstances?

3. Do I feel emotionally and mentally detached from my job?
4. Has there been a drastic decline in my enthusiasm and efficiency?
5. Have I been struggling to keep it together for the past few months?
6. Do I feel like my everyday life is just too fast for me?
7. Am I unable to concentrate on extremely mundane tasks?
8. Do I feel depressed?
9. Do I often feel the urge to drown my sorrows with potentially unhealthy habits like binge-watching, smoking, overeating, and excessive drinking?
10. Do I experience most of the symptoms described in the previous stages?

This set of questions requires utmost sincerity as they will enable you to track the progression of your personal or occupational burnout and ascertain whether you are progressively transitioning from one stage to the next. To achieve a more reliable diagnosis, check the symptoms you are experiencing with the symptoms discussed in chapter two.

Next, we will zoom into the complex psychological and emotional factors behind the manifestation of burnout to help you understand why and how the condition is peculiar for every individual.

CHAPTER 6

# UNDERSTANDING YOUR UNIQUENESS, WHY BURNOUT EXPERIENCES VARY WITH INDIVIDUAL

---

*Burnout is so hard to get out of because when you are in it, you ask yourself, what can I do to bring me relief from all the pressure and stress of all this work I need to do?' and the only answer you can think is, 'the only thing that will bring me relief is if I finish this work.*

JOHNNY SUN

---

The previous chapter required that you answer some questions sorted by the different stages of burnout, aimed at evaluating your current burnout status. A combination of your responses is expected to provide a substantial burnout diagnosis, which is essential in your journey to recovery. On the individual level, different people will have different answers to those questions; however, they may end up with a similar diagnosis. Two people may be burning out, but not in the exact same manner. What I am saying in essence, is that burnout does not happen to you and someone else the same way, irrespective of whether you have similar personalities or not. It is not rocket science—you are not them and they are not you. Your experience is peculiar to just you.

There are complex emotional and psychological factors behind this difference in burnout patterns. Recognizing these factors will help you modify your lifestyle and reduce your chances of overworking yourself to the point of burning out. It will also help you appreciate individual indifferences and understand why you may burn out faster than others, or why others can put up with a situation you cannot stand. You will understand the role you play in facilitating your burnout and how addressing these factors makes you responsible for your recovery. Ultimately, you have the power to pull yourself out from the vacuum where burnout holds you hostage, and the purpose of this book is to help you realize as well as harness your power.

We will now discuss the basic internal factors behind your unique burnout condition. They include mindset, perspective, approach to work/life, personality, and other peculiar conditions.

## MINDSET

The mind is where many (im)possibilities are explored—where perspectives, feelings, opinions, and beliefs are nurtured, resulting in a dynamic configuration. Through your mindset, you can prompt yourself to be a little braver, tenacious, promising, or productive. Likewise, your mindset can cause you to zone out when the task becomes unfulfilling and boring. You may not necessarily be unmotivated to work because the job is overly challenging, but because you have engineered your mind to believe it is difficult and you function based on this configuration. If you have decided within yourself that you are not cut out for mentally exhausting tasks, this becomes an extra roadblock on your path. Even if it is actually difficult, it will seem less surmountable with a negative mindset.

This fierce yet silent belief may be a contributor to your burnout condition. That intuitive voice within you screaming, "I can never do this!" may be why you struggle to find the energy and enthusiasm you need to get through the day. If you rewire your mind's voice to something more positive, you will instinctively muster more confidence and zeal to salvage the situation. Your problem would not miraculously shrink because you developed more enthusiasm to tackle it, but you may become more creative to the point that you develop a relevant solution.

At this juncture, there is something you must bear in mind. You must hold it close to your heart on this journey to overcoming burnout and repeat it for as long as you have to until your mind is marinated in it. It is known as the BURNOUT ALLEVIATION RULE and it goes thus:

**Among other things, never forget to assess your psychological approach to a situation before you assume that situation is burning you out.**

In other words, your approach could be lacking or the problem could be genuinely difficult, which is why you should always evaluate the situation with an unbiased mind to know if the problem is the way you are handling the situation. Ascertain what you can do better and go a step further to make a move in the right direction. The Burnout Alleviation Rule was birthed after an argument I had with my husband. I was livid and unsure of my role in that situation, unsure whether I had done the right thing. Later that day, I went out. I stopped to fill my tank in a gas station, and while I filled it, I kept ruminating about the argument, asking myself a train of questions and flipping tables.

I asked myself, "Okay, so there was a situation, quite all right. But did I overreact?", "If he had said what I said to him, how would I feel?" The answer became more obvious to me the more I thought about it. I could have handled the situation better. Eventually, I realized that I was navigating life with pent-up frustration and fatigue, constantly seeking an outlet, any opportunity to let it all out on someone or something.

### Positive vs. Negative: Do you see the glass as half-empty or half-filled?

A positive mindset is one that encourages positive thinking and anticipates positive results. You believe everything is ultimately working in your favor and will amount to greater good, even if it may not look like it all the time. This mentality leaves you with a half-filled glass. It may not be enough, but it will suffice and make sense somewhere ahead, so you chin up and address the situation with unwavering enthusiasm—or you overcome your fears and do it scared, as Ruth Soukup proposes in her book *Do It Scared: Finding the Courage to Face Your Fears, Overcome Adversity, and Create a Life You Love.* You do not have to be certain of the result or feel the absence of fear, but you are motivated to take action and hope for a great outcome. Positive thinking, as opposed to a negative mindset, has additional benefits. It increases the flow of cells responsible for your body's immunity, such as natural killer cells that target and eliminate virus and tumor cells, making you less susceptible to illness and acting as a substantive measure against serious diseases like cancer. Through positive thinking, you can create positive emotions, including happiness, joy, resilience, and contentment, subsequently reducing the intrusion of negative emotions like worry, anxiety, and anger.

On the flip side, a negative mindset leaves you always considering the worst possible scenarios, which may cripple your ability to take action. After all, what is the point of doing anything if everything looks bleak? If you do not see an endeavor yielding anything substantial, why get involved at all? This is the half-filled glass perspective. This mindset leaves us believing that life is unfair, especially to us. We believe things will go bad soon enough and actively anticipate the undoing of our efforts. It could be a defense against disappointment. I mean, if you expect the worst, then you may never be disappointed or heartbroken... right? It sounds plausible until the point you realize this school of thought leaves you wallowing in a cloud of gloom and joylessness. A negative mindset will expose you to stress, depression, and lack of enthusiasm. Constantly getting caught up in a loop of negative thoughts may be a factor of your environment. You probably did not choose to be grumpy and sad, which may make it more frustrating. To combat negative intrusion, you have to acknowledge it, observe it, and understand its origin. There are external factors that may result in the development of negativism, including social media, news, and even family. It may be difficult to stop our negative thoughts because they become such intimate parts of us and constantly infringe on our mental space before we even realize it.

Mindfulness and compassion are useful tools here; and as we progress, you will learn more about how to employ them in your burnout journey. For now, bear in mind that you possess the ultimate power over your mind. You can gain control. You can realign your thoughts. It is possible, and believing in yourself is the first step to true freedom.

---

> Besides an apple a day, a positive thought also keeps the doctor away.
>
> JULIA MIREN, AMERICAN FITNESS EXPERT

---

This may explain why a staggering number of people burn out. According to Forbes, more than half of people are unhappy in their jobs, and burnout will naturally germinate when people maintain a negative mindset, in this case, unhappiness.

While genetic and environmental factors may be involved in the development of a mindset, your mindset is primarily determined by you. You are in control of your situation, and you can decide whether the cup is half-filled or half-empty. And that is excellent news. The key is paying attention to your mind and understanding what thoughts sprout during your decision-making.

## PERSPECTIVE

Perspective simply means a point of view. It refers to how you process a situation, your environment and the people around you, and subsequently, it determines how you react to those. It determines the basis of your judgment and how you draw inferences. Perspective also reflects the extent to which you understand the world around you and the philosophies you have adopted throughout your life. The idea of perspective is in such a way that it is not observed from a rightness or wrongness standpoint. It is an individual notion, which in certain circumstances, can be flawed or rather acceptable. Two people can look at the exact same situation and have totally different perspectives, which will impact their reaction to it. For example, when burning out, you may tend to see everything as unsurmountable. This further exacerbates your burnout and deteriorates your condition.

## APPROACH TO WORK/LIFE

Your approach to work is significantly linked to your mindset and further rooted in your personality. Recognizing your approach towards work and life, in general, will help you reorient your method of managing burnout and the stressful situations in your daily life. To understand how burnout manifests in your life, your primary assignment is to understand yourself in great detail. Here are some common approaches to work:

### A. THE WORKAHOLIC

Burnout analyst Rachel Fin describes a workaholic as "one who is performance-oriented and often struggles with work-life integration." By extension, a workaholic is more concerned about achieving results and hitting milestones. They work long hours and often spill activities from work into their leisure period and quality time to be spent with their family or a partner. They check their work emails at odd hours, in the middle of the night or during holidays and measure their success by how hard they work. The first step to breaking this cycle is keeping track of time. Observe your productive and unproductive hours and break off work when you feel mental exhaustion; mental exhaustion hints at a productivity decline. Make it a habit to communicate to those around you when you feel burned out. Their empathetic gestures may convince you to take a break.

However, it is interesting to note that the workaholic does not exist in isolation from perfectionism, which brings us to the following approach to work.

## B. THE PERFECTIONIST

Perfectionism is a personality trait characterized by a person's striving for flawlessness and setting high-performance standards, along with critical self-judgment and concerns regarding the thoughts of others. A perfectionist is keen on getting absolutely flawless results that meet the criticism of everyone. They hate to be perceived as imperfect and the desire to meet the approval of others drives them to intense self-criticism. The result? I am sure you can guess. They overwork themselves and burn out.

The perfectionist wants to overachieve and is only interested in a work environment that delivers an impeccable finish. They know how it is done and get cranky when it is not done in the exact way they know to be correct. This sounds awesome since having quality delivery is the hallmark of a reliable work environment...doesn't it? Do not answer yet.

Instead, consider the perfectionist's encounter with an intern or a beginner. Beginners require patience, trust, and encouragement, which the perfectionist does not have a lot to spare at the expense of a stellar delivery. The perfectionist will set unrealistic standards for the beginner (including other people working with them) and eventually push them to the edge of frustration, anxiety, and self-doubt because they will never satisfy the perfectionist no matter how hard they try. The perfectionist will burn out and edge those working with them towards the same fate.

How does the perfectionist sound now? Still awesome? I guess your answer will be "not quite," irrespective of whatever benefits perfectionism offers. It is a deal with the devil: productivity at the expense of your sanity and wellbeing. If left unchecked, it is a ticking time bomb—a disaster chef. Mark Zuckerberg, CEO of Meta, says, "Don't even bother avoiding mistakes because you will make a ton of them." In essence, if you are too busy avoiding mistakes, picking out every error in a product, and mulling over flaws, you cannot move on to the next task. You will feel stagnant, unproductive, bored, frustrated, exhausted, and burned out.

If you feel like you are caught up in the perfectionism loop, one way to control the situation is to constantly remind yourself that the world is not perfect and you cannot have absolute control over everything. Look back and see how much you have accomplished. Reminisce on how far you have come and give yourself a pat on the back. Treat yourself to something nice. You could also keep a gratitude journal or an accomplishment journal. Keeping those will help you be less tensed and pressured by your inner drives since you will have an overview of your successes, rather than being burdened by regret and criticism from things you have not achieved yet.

## C. THE PEOPLE PLEASER

A people pleaser is everyone's go-to person. Do you need someone to quickly help you build a website? Take it to the people pleaser. Need someone to pick you up from the mall because your car suddenly broke down, call them. Need someone to babysit your children while you travel for a three-day conference? People-pleasing neighbor to the rescue. Whatever it is, just dial the people pleaser. Do you know why? They will always say YES. I like to call us (I am using us here because this used to be me) the *yesfolks* because of this, and it goes beyond plain kindness. People pleasers will go to absurd lengths to satisfy others, including tweaking their own lives.

Constantly taking drastic measures towards the happiness of others to your detriment will leave you stressed and anxious. Oftentimes, people-pleasing behavior is deeply rooted and may be due to trauma. For example, a person dealing with abandonment issues may struggle to please their partner, teacher, or parent to earn their approval and sustain the relationship. In the workplace, a people pleaser will take so many jobs at a time until they have no time spared for themselves, resulting in self-neglect. The implication is that such a person may become overwhelmed with responsibilities and assignments. It can become so intense that, at some point, they become frustrated. Yet, they do not stop taking up more assignments, not even when they are clearly burning out.

In situations like this, you must learn to set definite boundaries and enforce them. People will not respect your boundaries if you disrespect them by yourself. You need to draw the lines and set a standard of what you can accomplish at every point in time without overexerting yourself. If possible, delegate some of the tasks you have at hand or request an extension of your deadlines if it is mandatory that you accomplish them.

## D. THE NARCISSIST

According to Timothy J. Legg, Ph.D., "a narcissist is someone with narcissistic personality disorder (NPD), who has an inflated sense of importance, craves attention, lacks empathy, and cannot build a great relationship with anyone at the workplace or beyond."

To everyone else, a narcissist is selfish, self-absorbed and acts mindlessly towards matters pertaining to anyone other than themselves. However, the narcissist's perception of self is very far from this. They believe they are only trying to make things work and the other person is being stubborn, unyielding or irrational. They may not even realize how their actions affect others since they are often consumed with arrogance and cannot see past themselves. If there is a problem, then it is the other party—not them. They are often entitled and manipulative in nature and do not perform so well at caretaking jobs that require a good level of self-awareness and selflessness. Being in a relationship with a narcissist may be draining as they hardly try to understand things from your point of view.

Naturally, a narcissist is an overachiever and a perfectionist. An overachiever never takes a break and is always reaching for the next step of the ladder. They are never sure when to stop or when their strength will give way and keep pushing until they break down. If you recognize narcissism in yourself, burnout may be imminent. A good strategy that can help you navigate out of this self-absorbed state is to practice self-compassion. Stop comparing yourself to others, creating a standard for unnecessary comparisons that fuel your need for approval and recognition. To become more empathetic, you need to think about people as much as you think about yourself. Put yourself in the other person's shoes and determine how they will feel before you pronounce a decision. By evaluating how an action will make you feel, you may be compelled to apply more leniency in your approach.

## PERSONALITY

Your personality comprises your physical and emotional response to a situation. Some people are highly self-focused, overachieving, and would stop at nothing to achieve their desired results. This aggressiveness towards achieving their goals increases their thirst for power and significance, which drives them to work harder. This group of people is more liable to burnout.

Unhealthy dissatisfaction is also rooted in personality. You always want more, and you are easily bored until you take up responsibilities that are well above your capacity. Given that you belong to the category of people that are not easily satisfied, you will have trouble resting. Like an athlete, you are constantly on the run because a competitor is close or you have a target goal to meet by the year's end.

Carl Gustav Jung, Swiss psychiatrist, psychoanalyst, and founder of analytical psychology, proposes eight basic categories of human personalities: Extraverted Thinking, Introverted Thinking, Extraverted Feeling, Introverted Feeling, Extraverted Sensation, Introverted Sensation, Extraverted Intuition, and Introverted Intuition. This classification is widely accepted, and it is believed that if you belong to one category, it will take a toll on you when you work in a job outside your personality.

As an introvert, if you take up an affiliate marketing job or a public relations office, you are more likely to exhaust yourself and 'malfunction.' Similarly, an extrovert who does stock computing or programming may feel unfulfilled and bored, as these jobs require sitting at the same spot for long hours.

Some other psychologists group the human personalities into seven: King, Priest, Sage, Scholar, Warrior, Artisan, and Server. The central idea is that your personality will largely determine the type of work appropriate for you. If you are a King, you may be best suited to social and administrative roles. However, this cultural configuration does not imply that you are superior or inferior to any other personality. You are just better suited to something than someone with another personality type.

The Myers and Brigg's personality test is available online for free, so I invite you to look further into this. The test will help you learn more about your personality type and gain insight into how to approach your burnout experience and improve your work-life balance. Discovering who you are can help you realize why you overwork yourself in your job/relationship or why you may lose interest in the long run.

## PECULIAR CONDITION

People live through very different circumstances that impact their stress levels and mental wellness. You may have a massive student debt to clear. Mr. B may have overdue rent or utility bills, and Ms. K may have to complete a vital project within a tight deadline in addition to an underlying health condition. The need to meet these financial or contractual obligations may drive you to mental and physical exhaustion.

In some other situations, overworking may be a coping mechanism to mask an unsuccessful relationship or grief. Fear of dealing with your thoughts or interacting with people forces you to remain glued to work. Events may be unfolding at an extremely fast pace that you no longer have control over the situation. Sometimes, you simply have to accept that something is wrong and there needs to be a change. You need to accept that you have taken on more than you can handle and cannot continue like this.

## YOU ARE NOT ALWAYS RESPONSIBLE FOR YOUR BURNOUT

Before we wrap up this chapter and the first part of this book, it is important to establish that you may not be the only cause of your burnout. Previous chapters may have made you believe otherwise. We have discussed how you may burn out by adopting the wrong approach to your job expectations and how your overachieving, perfectionism or narcissistic tendencies may adversely affect you and others. We have discussed how pessimism may also hinder your progress, resulting in anxiety and burnout, and how the roles you take up affect your susceptibility to burnout.

I need you to know that your burnout is not always self-designed. There may be external contributors that may sometimes even be beyond your control. Your work environment is a typical example. If you work in a toxic environment characterized by a negative atmosphere created by co-workers, supervisors, or the company culture itself, it will be difficult for you to advance in your career path.

In her sensational leadership book, *Effective Nursing Leadership: A practical guide*, Virginia K. Ballie describes a toxic work environment as one where the goals are obscure, the values are irrelevant, communication is always defensive and aggressive, decision-making is constantly top-down, feelings of staff are discarded and neglected, listening is the staff job, and roles are confusing. This is not only about the demanding nature of the workplace; you will also feel insignificant and neglected. You are just another figure and you have to stick to the policies despite your frustration and helplessness. Oftentimes, you cannot change these toxic situations, and may just have to tap out. As mentioned earlier, while you may not be responsible for the toxic nature of your environment, it is your responsibility to find the strength to remove yourself from this situation.

It gets even trickier when neither party is responsible for the toxic situation. You may discover that you are not well suited for a job you enthusiastically applied for. Your partner may not be toxic. It may just be that your personalities, beliefs and principles are incompatible. It simply does not work. In the event of any of these external setbacks, do not be discouraged. Build yourself up again in tiny bits and heal. Take it as an opportunity for self-reflection.

Now that we have addressed how burnout originates, as well as its causes, pathophysiology and unique manifestation, we will delve into part two of this book, which discusses effective and feasible ways to overcome your burnout condition.

# CHAPTER 7
# YOUR MIND'S POWER

> Being overwhelmed means that your life or work is overpowering you. Regain control by clarifying your intentions, setting realistic expectation, and focusing on your next step
>
> DAPHNE MICHAELS

Previously, we discussed mindset as a key contributing factor to the manifestation of burnout, establishing that the mind is the nurturing ground for perspectives, feelings, opinions, and beliefs. A combination of these elements results in a dynamic configuration.

The mind is also the seat of consciousness, thought and awareness, from where you process the things happening around you, make decisions, and take action. There is a voice in your head and it is peculiar to every individual. When you go grocery shopping, you have internal conversations that result in the decision to buy or to not buy certain items. Likewise, you ponder people's utterances before you proffer a response and your response often reflects your ideology or mentality.

The mind is therefore a powerful human feature and the

essential tool required to fight burnout. Fatigue, addiction, stress, and many other burnout symptoms may seem physical, but they all stem from the mind. The enthusiasm and spark you felt at the start of your job or relationship originated from your mind and in the event of burnout, your mind will also be your greatest undoing because it resides at the core of your diminished excitement, uncertainty, decline in concentration and the unwillingness to persevere.

Right from the honeymoon stage, your mind plays an active role in the burnout process. It fuels your excessive drive and ambition, as well as your enthusiasm and motivation to work harder at the expense of everything else. By extension, the consequential apathy, mental fatigue and diminished enthusiasm are also rooted in your mind. You may ignore all the warning signs and red flags that indicate you are approaching your breaking point. Your mind may also fight against the obvious signs that suggest you are burning out, preventing early diagnosis and intervention. Hence, you should know that burnout recovery can only begin when you admit to the possibility of burning out rather than relying on pills to help you overcome the symptoms of burnout.

Acknowledging burnout as a psychological condition will heighten your consciousness and awareness toward your job, relationship, hobbies, strengths, weaknesses. This will help you realize how burnout can occur through these channels.

I did not consider my condition psychological until I felt my sanity was threatened and I began to feel physical pain in different areas of my body. After I took some tests online and did thorough research on my condition (which inspired me to develop the burnout evaluation test in chapter five), only then did I realize I was burning out. Prior to this, I always assumed I was simply having a bad day. I often spent long hours in the shower hoping to drown my worries and feel refreshed afterward. I could afford good sleep on some nights, but when I began to feel pains around my joints, I was forced to seek medical attention. I resorted to analgesics but none of these measures significantly improved my condition. Everything changed when I realized that I was not dealing with a physical condition.

While it may not be feasible to eradicate all the circumstances possibly triggering your burnout, it is possible to build resilience and mental strength. You may still have to work double shifts and return to take care of the kids. You may still have to divert most of your earnings into settling bills and debts, and you will have to keep working to put food on the table. This does not mean you cannot triumph over burnout.

**YOU CAN and YOU WILL.**

In the following pages, we will discuss some practical ways to harness the power of your mind as a weapon on your journey to defeating burnout. I learned these methods from interview sessions and documentaries of worldwide renowned psychologists, and I believe they may be instrumental to you. Remember, in the previous chapter, we discussed how burnout varies with each individual and how your uniqueness influences your susceptibility to burnout.

You should know that you do not need to adopt all the mind-enhancing techniques we are about to discuss; you only need to take what applies to your unique condition and incorporate it into your lifestyle. It is essential to understand what works for you and do just that.

## FORGIVENESS

You may be wondering what stake forgiveness has in the process of healing from burnout. To understand this, we need to reemphasize the link between burnout and loss of mental and emotional energy. When you no longer have the energy to perform simple tasks, you may harbor feelings of shame, frustration, annoyance and anger toward your diminished capacity. This is where forgiveness comes in. Forgiveness, has been linked to lower levels of depression, stress and anxiety, and can help you maintain your mental and emotional energy reserves. If you create an unforgiving environment for yourself where failure is unacceptable and mistakes beget intense self-criticism, you may just be setting yourself up for burnout. Unless you ascertain what ignites your feeling of resentment, you will not find peace, and neither will your burnout recovery journey be possible. You need to bring yourself to let go of the anger and frustration. Without doing so, you risk treading down a self-destructive path; feeling like you do not deserve good things in your life.

Forgiveness does not simply entail saying 'I forgive you.' It is about unpacking your heart and bringing out all the hurts, anguish and fury you have been nursing to create room for new energy, peace, and renewed sense of purpose. To heal, you must practice self-indulgence, accept that you are not perfect and realize that perfection is not a criterion for a fulfilled, happy life. In fact, perfectionism can steal your appreciative nature and leave you noticing only the downside of life, forgetting that life happens in highs and lows. You are here right now and cannot be in more than one place. Same as when you are at work. You are there and cannot be tending to your garden plants at the moment. You cannot be responsible for everything and everyone all the time. You cannot keep blaming yourself for the actions and decisions of others either. Put yourself in the spotlight and do what is best for you. It does not make you selfish. You do your best every day and that is what counts.

You cannot be available for others if you are unavailable for yourself. As a parent, your happiness should not be the ultimate sacrifice you make to secure your children's wellbeing. You too can be happy, and best believe your children will be happier when you are truly fulfilled. Seeing you suffer and struggle does no good for them. I, therefore, invite you to nurture creativity, understanding, and self-compassion. Remind yourself as often as possible that it is safe to make mistakes. What is most important is to learn from them.

Earlier on, I highlighted the benefits of journaling and how you can use it to improve your burnout recovery journey.

Throughout this chapter, you will find journal prompts to guide your self-evaluation and healing. Journal prompts are written questions, themes or topics that will help you get started with journaling. Using those journal prompts will give you a clearer direction of where to go and what to reflect on.

## *JOURNAL PROMPTS FOR FORGIVENESS*

We are our own worst critics which makes self-forgiveness difficult. We hold ourselves to higher and often unrealistic standards and expectations. These journal prompts can help you identify experiences and instances that require you to forgive yourself.

- Are you hard on yourself when you fail to meet your personal goals?
- Do you believe there is something you need to forgive yourself for?
- When you attack yourself with negative thoughts, take two steps back and pause. These negative thoughts often come in the form of statements that begin with "I always . . .", "I never . . .", "Everything...", "I'm such a . . ."
- Reflect on the situation or event that left you feeling frustrated or angry at yourself. Describe the sequence of events and elaborate how you felt in good detail. How has this anger or frustration affected you since then?
- It is easier to forgive yourself when you can be specific about what you want to let go of. Reflect on your tasks and goals. Are they realistic?
- Are you a forgiving person? Is it difficult for you to forgive others? If yes, why?
- When a situation or person triggers anger or frustration in you, put yourself in their shoes and try to

imagine the motive behind their action. Consider what you would have done if you were in their position. You may find that there is not much you would have done differently. This may encourage your spirit of forgiveness, empathy, and compassion.
- Write down three flaws about yourself that you have been able to accept. Reflect on what you have learned from them and consider how can you look at these flaws in a positive light.
- In what ways can you be more compassionate towards yourself?

## STRATEGIES FOR SELF-FORGIVENESS

- To forgive yourself, focus on your emotions. Acknowledge what you are upset about/what you blame yourself for and negotiate with your inner critic. Yes, you made a mistake, but everybody makes mistakes and the important thing is that you are willing to make it right. If possible, make a list of things you need to forgive yourself for. Note you will feel guilty, but I invite you not fight this guilt as it may be useful to foster remorse, which will, in turn, result in self-learning, personal development and internal change. Consider if there is any way you can make amends. If you spoke to someone harshly, consider reaching out to them with a heartfelt apology. It will help you feel better about the situation when you do.
- Consider your mistakes as valuable learning experiences that have the potential to improve your future. Think about three situations where you did the

best you could with what you had. It will help you forgive your shortcomings and move on.

- Once you decide to forgive yourself, seal it with an action. You can write about it in a journal, write yourself a letter, or even talk about it to someone you trust.
- Questioning yourself in an attempt to understand where you erred is a good thing. It may help you identify how to do better in the future. Forgiving yourself requires that you thoroughly process your emotions and thoughts. However, you should be careful to not get stuck in a self-criticizing bubble as you evaluate yourself. If you feel like you are stuck, pause and distract yourself with an activity that relieves you, like cooking, strolling or gardening.

## EXAMINING YOUR HABITS

Consciously examining your habits can help you distinguish helpful habits from those that downgrade your quality of life. Do you engage in it excessively to the point it becomes detrimental? When I was diagnosed with burnout, I took a step back to have a hard look at my habits. I could not fathom how I ended up in the firm clutch of burnout, and I was desperate to understand. When I looked deeper, I became aware of all the little bad habits I had created over the years. All the skipped meals, all the overworking hours, all the "I'll do it as soon as possible" I would say despite being already overwhelmed—it all seemed normal to me. Examining my habits made me see things in a new light. I, for example, realized I disliked putting off tasks more than anything, especially when I estimated the given task could be completed in a few minutes. I would rather make time to do it right away because it felt like the ideal thing to do. The tricky part was, it never ended in 30 minutes. I always needed a few more minutes to wrap things up. Along the line, something else surely popped up. So I would try to attend to that, and attending to that extra thing always led to something else. It was a never-ending, torturous loop that made me prone to burnout. If you recognize a similar tendency in yourself, you may want to pay closer attention to how this habit impacts your life.

Fortunately, you can improve your habits. American journalist and author, Charles Duhigg, says, "Once you understand that habits can change, you have the freedom and the responsibility to remake them." Adopting new habits does not necessarily entail deleting a bad habit; a more feasible approach may be to replace the bad habits with a better or more neutral habit.

## JOURNAL PROMPTS FOR EXAMINING YOUR HABITS

- Now that you have better understanding of burnout, pay keen attention to yourself and look out for patterns at work, at home and in your relationships. What habits are holding you back? Be completely honest with yourself.
- Reflect on what you are trying to achieve and why you adopted this habit.
- To keep your habits in check, create a habit tracker in your journal and fill in no more than three habits at a time. Items in your journal can include your daily water intake, daily meditation, mood, work, and daily steps. Do not be hard on yourself if you fail to reach your goal. The important thing is to stay aware and do your best. You could also create a not-to-do list to remind yourself of the habits you want to replace. This may include reducing your social media usage and the number of times you check you mail in a day.

## STRATEGIES FOR EXAMINING YOUR HABITS

- Have a conversation with your friends, family, and colleagues. Ask them what habits they think you have cultivated over the years (both positive and negative). It may be more effective to have a physical conversation, but if the thought of this makes you uncomfortable or jittery, you can simply write them a letter and wait for their response. You want this exchange to be constructive and sincere.
- Adopting new habits require commitment, patience, and self-discipline. Be realistic about the process and forgive yourself when you fall short of your goals.
- Try to engage your new habits frequently. The number of consistent days required to create a new habit not only varies with every individual, but also depends on the activity. Building a reading habit will not be as easy as learning to brush twice a day. However, 20 to 30 days of consistent engagement may be a good start regardless of whatever habit you want to adopt.
- Make your new habit the first thing you do daily. When looking to start a new habit, the simplest method is to start your day with that newly desired habit. This will reinforce the importance of this new habit in your brain and increase your chances of success.
- Schedule your habits on your calendar. When deciding to break a habit or begin a new one, you must be intentional. Make detailed, actionable schedules, from the exact action required to the time of the day the action will be carried out.
- Think of situations that can hinder your progress and plan to overcome them when they actually happen. If

you are fond of checking your mail or social media too frequently, you can disable notifications for mails and certain social media apps to prevent them from intruding. Schedule specific times to check your mail and messages. Putting this in place may help you gain better control of your mail-checking habit and social media usage.

## DEVELOPING MINDFULNESS

Mindfulness is the basic human ability to be fully present and aware of your body, feelings, thoughts, and surroundings. Our minds often wander and we may find ourselves obsessing over the past or the future, leaving us anxious, ashamed, or regretful. You may catch yourself behaving out of pocket, saying something unusual or making an impulsive decision in an emotional state without considering the consequence; often, you may regret these unusual actions. Think of one time you made a decision without thinking it through—without fully realizing the outcome, or situations where you let yourself be swayed by your circumstances or by others, simply because you did not object.

By not listening to your gut and pausing to examine your actions, you risk existing on autopilot and walking away from the life you desire. Not living in accordance with your needs, values and desires, will leave you feeling empty, unhappy, and lonely. In the event of burnout, you may tend to stop listening to yourself as burnout results in a collapse of consciousness. Whether you stop listening to yourself because you are burning out, or because it is something you were never conscious of, the result is the same: You shut down your mind's voice which raises an energy depletion alarm and cover it up with the voice of ego and perseverance that edges you on, assuring you that you « can do it all ». I often found myself in a state of complete denial, pulling through situations that clearly harmed me, but seeing nothing wrong with them because they had become integral parts of my life.

An Australian study, shows mindfulness meditation significantly increases awareness of the present moment and attention to physical tension, improves focus and promotes less preoccupation with the past and future. Participants also noted improvements in their sleep quality, a normalization of their blood pressure, and an increased ability to handle difficult matters in the workplace.

Mindfulness will improve acceptance of your current state, manage your emotions, strengthen your ability to cultivate compassion and a non-judgmental attitude toward yourself and others. Personally, mindfulness helped me navigate all the guilt, frustration and shame I felt for not being productive and focused enough. Additionally, listening to yourself will help you set boundaries and make the right decisions for you, including saying NO when you need to.

Incorporating mindfulness and self-awareness into your life can be laborious and intimidating. It requires great patience and focus. Notwithstanding, I want you to know that you are capable of mindfulness—anyone is. When you learn the principle of mindfulness, it will become one of your greatest assets on your journey to fulfillment. The good news is, that mindfulness is not a special activity that requires any physical setup as you would imagine meditation to be. It can be done anywhere and anytime.

## JOURNAL PROMPT FOR DEVELOPING MINDFULNESS

- Take five minutes to write down how you are feeling today. Are you feeling anxious or stressed? Is there tension anywhere in your body right now?
- Pay close attention to this moment and harness your five senses. What can you see? What can you smell? What do you hear?

- What three emotions do you feel as you write this?
- Reflect on how your day progressed. Did you feel connected and aligned to yourself, or were you simply breezing through the day?
- How can you improve the alignment between your thoughts and actions?
- Are there recent instances where you were absentminded in your interaction with the people you care about?
- Are your negative thought patterns linked to certain times of the day, energy levels, or activities?
- Is there anything you would want to do differently in your life?

## STRATEGIES FOR DEVELOPING MINDFULNESS

- Pick a daily activity and pay keen attention to how you execute it. It could be brushing your teeth, creaming your body, or organizing your desk. If you like to stroll, make a deeper observation of your environment the next time you go for a walk. Notice the things around you rather than simply glossing over the scenery. You may be surprised at what interesting details you have been missing all along.
- **If you have five minutes to spare during your day, I suggest you integrate this short practice into your schedule:**

1. Take a seat. Ideally, you want to find a calm and quiet place. You can sit on a chair with your feet touching the floor, or sit cross-legged on the floor. The goal is to

attain a position you can be comfortable in for a while.

2. Define a time limit. For beginners, I suggest starting with five minutes.
3. Acknowledge your body. Scan your body from head to toe, noticing the parts that are tense or at ease.
4. Feel your normal, uncontrolled breath. Notice the sensation of each inhale and exhale.
5. Start to deepen your breath, inhaling for 5 seconds, and exhaling for 5 seconds.
6. Notice when your mind wanders. Your attention will inevitably shift to other places. When you realize it, simply return your attention to your breath.
7. Be gentle to yourself and your wandering mind. Do not judge or be harsh on yourself. You do not want to obsess over the content of the thoughts you wandered to. Rather, you simply want to always come back.

## POSITIVE THINKING

Positive thinking entails approaching life with a positive outlook. It does not necessarily mean avoiding or ignoring the unpleasant aspects of life; rather, it involves making the most of a potentially terrible situation, believing in yourself and your abilities, and trying to see the best in other people.

The 2016 Journal of Behavioral Research and Therapy noted that most respondents reported greater happiness, restfulness and decreased anxiety as they begin to visualize positivity when they encounter depressing situations. Similarly, a study from the University of Kentucky established that positive thinking leads to more success, peace and inner comfort among respondents. German Lutheran Pastor, Dietrich Bonhoeffer, says, “The essence of optimism is that it takes no account of the present, but it is a source of inspiration, of vitality and hope where others have resigned; it enables a man to hold his head high, to claim the future himself and not to abandon it to his enemy."

Begin to focus on aspects of your life that are positive and exciting. Focus on the prospect that it assures in the next few years. Build a level of optimism that surpasses the pressures, fatigue, and the bad days. This is another practical way to improve your burnout and revive your enthusiasm. It will work in your relationship, parenting, or other aspects of life that burn you out.

Optimism wanes, and you must be prepared to motivate yourself all over. This is not an easy thing to do. On some days, you may feel so low on energy that getting out of bed will be a miracle. Living through burnout day by day already requires superhuman energy. However, negative and unconscious thoughts will worsen the situation. They poison your mind, lower your self-esteem, and breed negative feelings like fear and anxiety.

As humans, we tend to get lost in our thoughts and the stories they fabricate. If our unconscious thoughts tell us that we are worthless, we believe it. If they tell us that we are the most intelligent in the room, we also believe it. The good news is, the brain is a muscle, and like all muscles, you can strengthen and guide your mind's natural tendency toward optimism, rather than pessimism.

You can fight burnout and depression by disempowering negative thinking. To do so, you need to adopt a positive mentality and more importantly, stop believing those negative thoughts. When you discard negative thoughts, you allow your positive thoughts to fuel you with much-needed strength to go about your day. Practicing positive thinking through meditation and journaling will help you realize that everything is not dark and uninteresting.

## JOURNAL PROMPT FOR POSITIVE THINKING

- Identify your negative thoughts, then write them in your journal. Do this every time a negative thought pops into your mind. This will stimulate your awareness of these negative thoughts and give you the necessary distance to assess, challenge, and analyze them more objectively.
- At the end of the day, reread each negative thought and reflect on them. Is there evidence that proves the truthfulness of these thoughts? Can you think about any time this was proved wrong? For example, if you believe you are a total disaster at social events, try recalling times you felt at ease among people to combat the negative thought. You may find that you are not as socially awkward as you think.
- Look for patterns within your negative thoughts. Do your thoughts contribute to low self-esteem and a negative self-image?
- If your negative thoughts revolve around a situation or event, reflect on that event with the objective of digging up positive elements. We often convince ourselves that 'everything' went wrong. But did **everything** really go awfully wrong? Can you recall at least one thing that went right?

## STRATEGIES FOR POSITIVE THINKING

- Observe your thoughts daily. If you notice you have negative thoughts, make a conscious effort to reframe your thought in a more positive way. If you have a meeting with your boss tomorrow and cannot stop thinking of how unprepared you are, reframe your thought in this direction: The presentation is finished. I did my best, and there is nothing more I can do to make it better. I am professional and qualified enough to do this.

- Every time a negative thought rears its head, do something to consciously acknowledge it. You can write the time and thought in your journal, or move your bracelet from your left wrist to your right wrist. This will help your brain assimilate the information.
- Do not judge your negative thoughts or try to stop them. By doing so, you will simply multiply them. Make peace with your negative thoughts and do not be afraid of them. Accept them without judgement, while learning to stop believing them.
- Start each day by complimenting yourself. That moment when you look in the mirror in the morning is the perfect opportunity to compliment yourself. Be specific and sincere. Tell yourself the things you would want to hear from someone else: "I am intelligent. I am going to rock my presentation this morning. I am loved by my partner, children and close friends; they bring me a lot of love every day. I am doing my best in this moment. I am doing just fine." You can write these affirmations in sticky notes and paste them at different parts of your house to serve as a constant reminder.

## CULTIVATING GRATITUDE

Gratitude is a positive emotion that implies being thankful of things in our lives. You can experience gratitude by expressing your appreciation toward people, objects, things, and moments. Cultivating a sense of gratitude can help you sustain a more positive mood and also has social benefits. Researcher Chih-Che Lin found that a high level of gratitude has a strong positive impact on psychological well-being and depression. Another research, by Rash, Matsuba, and Prkachin in 2011 also reported greater life satisfaction and self-esteem in participants manifesting gratitude.

It is a natural human tendency to focus on the negative aspects of every situation. To worsen things, the symptoms of burnout particularly make it difficult to manifest gratitude, redirecting our focus to negativity as well. Personally, you may do too much at once and struggle to align with the fast pace at which your life unfolds, leaving you with little to no personal moments of reflection and gratitude. If you create time to ponder your relationship and your work, you will find several things to be grateful for, irrespective of the obstacles you may be facing.

Overlooking your reasons for gratitude exposes you to the negative and uninteresting parts of your work. You become so overwhelmed, that the little things that once mattered no longer seem significant. You fail to realize that waking up every day and being healthy are more than enough reasons to be grateful. I truly believe gratitude is a beautiful life concept. It helps you see life through the lens of little miracles and puts you in a better position to cherish whatever life you lead.

On days when you think everything is going wrong, writing about what you are thankful for revives you. When life already feels great, a gratitude journal reminds you of who supported you, helped you, and encouraged you in difficult times. However, you should know that being grateful does not mean you should neglect your feelings or refuse to admit when you are not okay. You can be grateful while being transparent enough with yourself to admit that you are experiencing hard times.

I'll also advise you to beware of comparisons. You may compare yourself to people you feel are doing better, have achieved more, are wealthier, or closer to achieving their goals than you are to achieving yours, but comparisons will often make you feel inferior rather than inspired. If you started yoga three months ago, comparing yourself to someone who has been practicing yoga for several years is not helpful. Quit looking over your shoulders to see what others are doing and focus on what you can accomplish from where you are, as well as what you have already accomplished.

## *JOURNAL PROMPT FOR CULTIVATING GRATITUDE*

- What nice thing did someone do for you this week?
- Write down three people you are grateful for. Afterward, make a list of what makes each of these three people special to you.
- List three things that always put a smile on your face.
- What are you most grateful for about your body and health? Identify them and explain why. You could be grateful for your feet because they take you anywhere. They help you walk, hike, workout, practice yoga and visit beautiful places.
- What aspects of your job do you love most?
- Write about something you accomplished today (professionally or personally). Why did you feel accomplished? How do you feel about it now?
- Every day, list three things you are grateful for. They can be little things like a stranger smiling at you on your way to work or a compliment from your partner. They can also be more significant things like having a roof over your head, having a functional and healthy body, and being lucky enough to sleep in a warm bed. I suggest you do this in the morning or at night before going to bed.

## STRATEGIES FOR CULTIVATING GRATITUDE

- When you notice yourself ruminating over a negative event or situation in your life, try to think of three things related to the situation that you are grateful for.
- To avoid comparing yourself to others, limit your time on social media and focus on your strengths. Think of five things about yourself that makes you unique. Write them down and revisit them whenever you question your worth or essence.
- Add a gratitude section to your journal. A gratitude section is a beautiful inventory of happy memories and things to be grateful for. You can rely on your gratitude section to provide comfort when things get difficult.

## RESILIENCE

Resilience is the ability to adapt in the event of adversity. It is the ability to recover after being given a reason to fall and languish in defeat. For everyone who has been through trauma, crisis, or heartbreak, you would know that resilience is an integral aspect of breakthrough. Certain situations can impose roadblocks on your path. It could be a traumatizing experience that left you with a huge scar, a terrible relationship, or derogatory remarks you received when you shared your ideas with your superior. Situations like these can have lasting impact on your motivation, enthusiasm or creativity. Resilience will help you navigate these situations that have potential to break you.

One thing you should know though is that resilience is not restricted to past situations. It also means adjusting to new realities. As described by the American attorney, Elizabeth Edward, "resilience is accepting your new reality, even if it's less good than the one you had before. You can fight it, you can do nothing but scream about what you've lost, or you can accept that and try to put together something that's good."

In burnout prevention or recovery, building resilience means accepting the situation, finding ways to heal from it, and establishing strategies to prevent relapse. It also significantly entails thwarting the after-effect of the burnout you have experienced. Forgiveness, mindfulness, and positive thinking can help you be more resilient. Be alert and attentive to your needs. Reread this chapter as often as you need to and keep journaling. Return to your journal whenever you need a reason to keep going.

It gets easier with time. You will get used to listening to yourself. You will get through this setback. You will adapt to the situation and emerge stronger. But you have to be convinced of it as well. So, say it out loud to yourself now: I CAN DO THIS AND I WILL.

Forgiveness, positivity, mindfulness, gratitude, and resilience will not matter if you do not transform them into habits. They are not one-off requirements. They must become habitual to yield substantial results.

Habits are essential for burnout recovery. Whatever method you choose to address your burnout must be cultivated into a long-term habit before you can expect significant changes.

Lou Holtz says, "It is not the load that breaks you down, it is the way you carry it." Shifting your mindset is essential when trying to get a different result. As you adopt gratitude, forgiveness, and empathy, adjust your mindset to one that enables you to see beyond the hurts and the obstacles.

# CHAPTER 8
# THE HEALING POWER OF SELF-CARE

*Sometimes, the most crucial thing in a whole day is the rest we take between two deep breaths*

ETTY HILLESUM

---

There is a definition of self-care I find particularly compelling and relevant. I am referring to Arin Murphy-Hiscock's famous description, which says, "Self-care means considering yourself a worthwhile person and presenting yourself as valuable, capable, and deserving. In other words, self-care seeks to redress an imbalance that develops when you don't take proper care of yourself, whether by inattention or by choice."

Let us dissect this definition. Arin suggests that self-care comprises two primary segments: Your conscious attempt to accept that you are valuable, capable, and deserving; and your conscious attempt to correct an imbalance in your system that generates intentionally or as a result of negligence. Accepting and loving yourself may seem simple at a superficial level, but ironically, many people do not realize how much self-hate, self-judgment, and rejection they inflict on themselves. They do not realize how desperate they are to be someone else—anything other than themselves, resulting in low self-esteem and at worst, an overall loss of identity.

You may not realize how far down the rabbit hole you have deviated until you reflect on your life and notice how you are no longer who you used to be. This digression is generally illustrated with the 'being a shadow of oneself' metaphor. A typical instance where you can digress is when you go out of your way to beat unrealistic and often unnecessary standards. Between the honeymoon stage and the onset of stress, you may notice some challenges or red flags, and determine that you are willing to invest in the situation and make the best out of it. With time, the weight on your back may intensify and you will begin to feel dismantled and uninterested in partaking, but reluctant to let go regardless of the growing challenge and suffering because the situation or person—perhaps a partner—has been greatly infused into your life and identity.

Entitlement can also set in when you have gone out of your way to normalize an activity at your workplace or relationship. When you no longer work extra hours, your boss may begin to feel you are slacking, meanwhile it was never in your job description. Your partner may also not understand why you suddenly backed out of what you have taught them to rely on you for. Situations like these have strong potential to precipitate burnout. This is where you must deploy the power of self-care to your rescue.

Self-care connotes recognizing your importance and understanding the key role you play in your life and overall wellbeing, realizing that no one else can fill that gap. You learn how to adopt the 'relax and recharge' principle. You learn to not overexert yourself. In physics, the stress-strain elasticity graph is a good way to describe overexertion and how you can exhaust yourself if you do not prioritize self-care. This graph tests the strength or limit of an elastic material when subjected to stress. First, there is the proportional limit where everything is normal. Think of this as the honeymoon stage. More pressure results in the material reaching its elastic limit, beyond which the stretched material can no longer return to its original form. This is where it gets interesting, where the yield point sets in with further exertion. The yield point is the start of deformation, or if you may, when you begin to lose your identity (onset of stress). Subsequently, the yield point amounts to the ultimate stressing point, which is the highest level of permissible stress before total breakdown (chronic stress). Any further applied pressure at this point results in the breaking point—a state of failure and complete loss of identity (burnout).

It is obvious that self-care is crucial to your burnout recovery journey. It is a potent remedy that can transform your life from a place of disinterest, pain, and frustration to a place of restoration, fulfillment, wholesomeness, and pure joy. We will now discuss the various ways to utilize self-care in your burnout journey.

## REST

Rest simply entails switching from activity to a state of relative inactivity. Take note of the phrase 'relative inactivity.' This means you do not necessarily need to be immobile or fixed in a position while you rest. For some, resting can involve leisure activities like strolling, cycling, going to the spa, walking their dog, gardening, simply sunbathing out in the balcony, sketching, or doodling. You will learn more about this as the chapter progresses. Whatever resting means for you, it is paramount that your brain is in a relaxed state, compared to when you are actively working. Rest and work must be in a constant dynamic for you to exist optimally. If you work eight hours a day, you do not need to rest for another eight hours. Rest and work do not balance out that way. A half-hour to one-hour rest can provide sufficient relief. You should also ensure that whatever time you allocate for resting must strictly involve only resting.

A Philadelphia medical doctor, Heather J. Moday, emphasizes that "making time for rest can recharge your ability to deal with commitments, relationships and impact your overall health." In other words, rest replenishes your enthusiasm and renews your energy, so that you can return to work again. Unfortunately, many people are scared to take time off because they believe their manager may be repulsive and feel that wanting to rest may cost them serious sanctions and ultimately, their job position. I particularly laud superiors that encourage rest because, at the end of the day, everyone wins. When individuals have sufficient rest, they are recharged, more efficient, happier, and more willing to work. This will definitely reflect on the individual's input and consequently, the company's output, progress, and growth. Overworking on the other hand only results in emotional, mental and physical decline, as well as possible breakdown.

Rest will reduce your stress and anxiety. It also decreases blood pressure, inflammation, and provides momentary relief from chronic pain. Your confidence, creativity, and short-term memory will also experience significant boosts when you improve your resting habit. A study conducted by a team at Heriot-Watt University in Scotland, funded by the Alzheimer's society, shows that resting for 10 minutes after learning something new increases your chances of retention, also discovering that quiet rest will not only help you retain new information but also retain detailed memory. Perhaps, the most exciting fact about rest is that if you rest enough, you may have no reason to despise the job that initially intrigued you. Sadly, we are often too carried away with life to realize how much our bodies crave even the littlest break.

You do not disappoint anyone when you rest. Your child does not expect you to break your back in an attempt to keep things together, your partner does not think you are lazy, and your boss is probably not foaming at the mouth in their office because you are resting after working tirelessly for several hours—and if they are, that is not your problem at all. You are doing nothing wrong. Rest is not a privilege; it is a necessity.

When I was at the peak of my burnout, I thought I had to keep pushing no matter what. I thought I had to persevere through all the things that caused me suffering, and my therapist asked me one question: If you had cancer, would you keep working or would you take time off to heal and take care of your body?

That question left me dumbstruck. Till today, I still ask myself that question when I am tempted to 'do an extra hour,' or 'finish working on one more document' when I should be resting or taking a break from work. It is your responsibility to take care of yourself. Your mental and physical health depends on your ability to say NO and rest. What is the essence of all your achievements when you are not well enough to enjoy them? The goal is to be reliable by showing up for yourself first and preserving your mental and psychological wellness. If you feel guilty about taking a break even though you realize you overwork yourself, consider seeking external views on it. This can give you a different perspective and help you recover faster from burnout. You may feel like you can handle everything and in the event that you do not, you may feel inadequate, whereas, you may be assuming more responsibility than you can accommodate at the time. Nonetheless, you will still feel like the problem is you—like you are overreacting and exaggerating the situation. It may be reassuring to have people validate your condition and help you realize that you are not inventing your suffering, and neither are you inadequate.

American therapist, Emma Reedy, says, "While I appreciate the concept that the opinion of others is not what gives us value, it is a harmful idea that we must not seek positive, validating messages from others when we are feeling down. After all, our inner voice—often showing up as an inner critic—is the internalization of our environment, including explicit and implicit messages from those around us." Seek the counsel of your friends, family, or colleagues. Talk about your struggles, especially when you find yourself in a receptive community. If you are still not convinced or do not get satisfactory opinions, consider professional help.

Now that we have established the importance of rest, we need to discuss the different forms of rest. As explained by the TED Talk speaker, Saundra Dalton-Smith M.D., there are at least seven types of rest, but we will be discussing six of them in this chapter. Employing a healthy aggregate of the various forms of rest will yield the best result.

## TYPES OF REST

### A. PHYSICAL REST

Physical rest involves resting the visible parts of our body, from the arms to the legs, neck, waist, and joints. You can rest these parts actively or passively. When you rest passively, there is no movement. Every joint in your body is relieved from pressure, with your internal organs being the only parts functioning. Active rest requires you to use one or more of your body parts, but it is still stress-free. It includes activities that help you stretch your body, improve your joints, and generally provide therapeutic effects. Stretching, Yoga and Massage Therapy are common examples. It is easy to tell when you need physical rest. You will feel pains in several joints or crucial parts of your body. You may feel your knees wobble, your fingers may hurt, and you may experience discomfort in your neck region and spine, especially after prolonged sitting.

I used to think I had superpowers and my body was extraordinary. I would feel physical pains, but still find it in me to go a little longer, resulting in chronic pains that even pills could not resolve—at least, not permanently. The most sensible thing to do when you feel physical discomfort is to rest.

### B. MENTAL REST

Mental rest is as crucial as physical rest. It refers to the deliberate attempt to rest your mental energy. This is crucial to avoid a condition commonly described as "brain fog." According to Merriam Webster, "brain fog is a usually temporary state of diminished mental capacity marked by an inability to concentrate or think or reason clearly." I think of it as that slow mental exhaustion that stealthily creeps on you after you have been working at stretch for a few hours. It slows you down and makes your brain foggy, then slowly grinds your productivity to a halt.

Brain fog occurs you work for prolonged hours without taking a break. It is not a severe medical condition; it is simply your brain's signal that it needs rest. If you work nine to five, you may experience brain fog early in the afternoon between 1 p.m. and 2 p.m. You will probably yawn a few times and feel numbness around a few joints. Your productivity will dwindle, and it will take longer to complete tasks that you would ordinarily accomplish within a shorter duration. To avoid reaching this point, take a few minutes of recess every couple of hours. There is no specific formula to it. The nature of your job determines the length and frequency of your breaks. If you work eight hours daily, you can take 15-minute breaks after every 1½ hours of work. These short breaks help you disconnect from your task, reset your brain, and improve blood flow throughout your body. You could stand and stretch for two minutes, take a few deep breaths, or go grab a bottle of water.

Some productive ways to get mental rest include taking a brief walk, grabbing a snack, and shifting attention to yourself. To center yourself, you can recline into a comfortable state and observe your breathing, joints, and heartbeat. I suggested this to my colleagues as a project manager, and they all admitted it worked wonders. They were refreshed and prepared to face the challenge with new energy when the break was over.

However, if you are going to grab a snack, ensure that your choice of snack is healthy and energizing. Also, coffee is not a snack to rely on.

## C. SENSORY REST

Sensory rest is a psychological attempt to rest your sensory system. The sensory system comprises the sense organs (eyes, nose, skin, ears, and mouth) and the internal parts of your body that facilitate its function. From birth, we are constantly using at least one of our senses, which makes it not so surprising that we may experience overwhelm and sensory fatigue sometimes. Blurry vision, irritation toward physical contact, adverse reaction to loud noise, and reduced sense of smell are signs of sensory fatigue. However, there are different ways you can rest each of your senses. The first step is to unplug. This could mean scheduling a time to disconnect from your phone, television, radio, and other electronic devices. Try using dark mode on your phone and laptop, or wear an eye mask to sleep; this could block out excessive light.

If you are surrounded by noise every day—for example, screaming toddlers, the noise of cars in traffic, the revving of machine parts—you need to engage in moments of silence or at least, moments where you can appreciate healthier sounds. You can plug into soothing music in the evenings, or take a stroll. Go outside. Experience nature; the birds chirping, the wind quietly gushing, or the sound of a bullfrog croaking in a nearby pond. These are sounds that can induce calmness and promote sensory rest. To rest your sense of taste, you can reduce your consumption of processed foods and opt for more natural recipes. Treat yourself to something delicious and exciting, and do not forget to savor every bit of the taste. The world will almost always be fast and overwhelming. You need to unplug from this rat race and find some time to replenish yourself.

## D. CREATIVE REST

Creativity is a spectacular human trait through which original ideas are generated. If your job demands a high level of creativity, brainstorming, and critical thinking, you can exhaust yourself;

although, creativity may seem inexhaustible. After all, to utilize it, you do not have to move around or do any strenuous physical activity. But you should know that just as physical energy can be depleted, creative energy can be depleted, too. Saundra Dalton-Smith, author of *Sacred Rest: Recover Your Life, Renew Your Energy, Renew Your Sanity*, says, "Humans need physical, mental, social, creative, emotional, spiritual, and sensory rest." A practical approach to creative rest is engaging in more leisure activities like dancing, reading, strolling, or hiking a few meters. Anything that distracts you from actively engaging in critical thinking can help you rest creatively.

## E. EMOTIONAL REST

Emotional stress is a reaction to the pressures of everyday life, marked by signs such as irritability, anger, loss of appetite, avoidance, and a feeling of hopelessness. You may be concealing your emotions, mentally strained, overworking, and pretending that your day is going just great when everything is absolutely going south. This is even truer if you are a helping professional. You do not want to be caught crying while teaching people to stop the tears. You have to pretend you are not bothered by a situation presented by your client. Then there are people pleasers, as we discussed earlier, who cannot say NO to requests. They agree to everything requested of them for fear of hurting others, failing to realize that they are hurting and exposing themselves to emotional burnout. A proven method to release emotional stress is letting it out. You could speak to a counselor or therapist about your struggles and frustration—even a friend or family member you are comfortable with can serve as a great solace.

## F. SOCIAL REST

Social rest is a way to establish balance in your social life to prevent it from eroding your mental and personal balance. As an extrovert, you should afford yourself more "me time" to enable you critically assess your personal life, meditate, and re-strategize. Are you an introvert? You can retire from your confines and be among a comfortable crowd. If as an introvert you assume a role that requires interpersonal relationships, you may find them tasking, uninteresting, and eventually burnout. The best fix for such situations is pausing and reclining to your initial personality as often as you can. Remember that when you rest frequently, you are revitalized and can seamlessly go about your life.

## JOURNAL PROMPTS FOR RESTING

- Go through the types of rest and reflect on which type of rest you need most right now. Do you feel physically, mentally, or emotionally exhausted?
- "Resting can be productive." How does this statement make you feel?
- At the end of a day off, do you feel rested and ready to resume work? If not, what do you need to change about how you spend your time off to encourage real rest?
- After deciding the type of break you need, consider the duration of rest. Will the weekend be enough? Do you need a longer break?
- What gives you the most energy and inspiration?

## STRATEGIES FOR RESTING

- Write down a few activities that interest you. Select one of them and find a way to incorporate it into your schedule this week.

Remember to note how you feel
before and after the activity.

- After determining the type of rest you need, schedule that type of rest in your agenda. Be specific, realistic, and respect the goal you set for yourself. I have shared some helpful tips on the different types of rest below.
- To mentally rest, plan a break every hour and a half throughout your work day.
- Have you ever tried closing your eyes for a fleeting moment? You may not know it, but by doing so, you have rested one of your receptive organs. Make a conscious effort to unplug from electronics during the day. Intentional moments of sensory deprivation can begin to undo the damage inflicted by our over stimulating world.
- Turn your workplace into an inspiration by displaying artworks of places, people, and things that speak to you. Consider starting activities such as embroidery, knitting, or ceramics.^

## NUTRITION/HYDRATION

Alongside rest, nutrition is one of the most critical aspects of self-care. Nutrition determines your intelligence, mood, energy level, and rate of success/failure. As Jean Anthelme Brillat-Savarin, French lawyer and politician would say, "Tell me what you eat, and I will tell you who are." People erroneously assume that eating simply entails putting something into one's stomach when a pang of hunger strikes. We forget that our bodies are complex and ignore the significant impact of our digestive system on our overall wellbeing, especially considering that every part of our body is intricately connected. For this reason, listening to your body, eating right, and consuming foods that make you feel good are important for you to monitor your energy intake, reduce fatigue, and boost your mental state.

Monitoring your eating habits does not mean you have to be strict with your diet. In a situation where you simply want to improve your dietary intake, you only have to be more conscious of what you eat, and understand how your feeding choices can impact your overall wellbeing. The former Harvard Medical School instructor, Dr. Eva Selhub, explains that, "multiple studies have found a correlation between a diet high in refined sugars and impaired brain function—and even a worsening of symptoms of mood disorders, such as depression." Another Harvard Health Publishing study suggests that "the brain has a direct effect on the stomach and intestines. For example, the very thought of eating can release the stomach's juices before food gets there. This connection goes both ways. A troubled intestine can send signals to the brain, just as a troubled brain can send signals to the gut. Therefore, a person's stomach or intestinal distress can be the cause or the product of anxiety, stress, or depression. That's because the brain and the gastrointestinal (GI) system are intimately connected."

In essence, what you put into your body has a significant impact on your health and sets the foundation for how you are going to feel that day or night (energetic, alert, tired, or enthusiastic). This implies a need to consume healthy, satisfying foods, not necessarily based on what society categorizes as good or bad, but based on how your body reacts to food and your specific need. To do this, you have to pay attention to how you feel before and after eating certain foods. Your body has the ability to detox and digest, so you do not have to be excessively stringent. Focus on what makes you feel healthy, alive, and energetic.

Before I quit my role as a senior accountant, I used to skip breakfast and grab a little lunch. My husband would make dinner, and I would just munch on whatever I found after the kids went to bed. In those circumstances, it is easy to ignore the damage you are inflicting on your body, but your body is always telling you how much your lifestyle favors you or does not; you only have to pay more attention. As part of your effort towards improving your burnout, it is essential to start listening to your body and learn what it wants—what is good for you. When we get so used to not listening, we begin to suffer for it through discomforts and depleted states of mind and body. Become more conscious of what you eat and how you eat it. Notice how your body responds to each food you consume and avoid foods that leave you feeling uncomfortable and depleted.

## MORE WATER, LESS COFFEE

Do not underestimate the importance of water in your system. It is a daily necessity. Water is required for digestion and bowel movement, maintaining the balance of your body fluids, as well as the elimination of toxins that can result in gastrointestinal inflammation and discomfort. On the other hand, coffee can cause a dramatic increase in your blood pressure by stimulating your nervous system. High caffeine intake is also associated with an increased risk of cardiovascular disease, anxiety, trembling and palpitations.

## JOURNAL PROMPTS FOR NUTRITION AND HYDRATION

- Reflect on your relationship with food and how you eat. How do your eating habits affect your daily life, social life, relationships, and overall mood?
- Are you mindful when eating?
- Do you put pressure on yourself to eat a certain way?
- Stress eating refers to the habit of eating (often unhealthy foods) to overcome the feeling of stress. Do you use food to de-stress? If yes, what emotions trigger you to eat?

- What would "healthy eating" look like to you?

Here are some specific prompts you can use before and after eating:

- How hungry are you before eating? Are you eating for nourishment or for other reasons such as relieving negative feelings?
- What are you thinking or feeling at the moment?
- How does your food taste, smell and feel? Are your enjoying each bite?
- Do you feel satisfied, hungry, or too full after eating?
- What are you thinking or feeling after eating?
- Do you check your phone or watch a movie while eating? These are habits that reduce your consciousness and lead to overeating or undereating.

## STRATEGIES FOR NUTRITION AND HYDRATION

- If you feel emotional, try talking to someone about it, or resort to self-care activities like yoga, meditation or journaling instead of compensating with food.
- Pay attention to how food tastes, smells and feels while eating.
- Eat in a way that is enjoyable and not restrictive. Notice your body signals. Eat slowly to allow your body react and digest food, and pause for a few breaths between bites to ensure you eat in full consciousness.
- Limit distractions and savor your food.
- Aim for a daily water intake of at least 10 cups per day, irrespective of your weight.

- Skipping meals is not a long-term solution. Honor your health by honoring your hunger.
- Make it a habit to drink a glass of water every time you drink coffee.

## SLEEP

Sleep is a vital part of rest. It allows you to reset and refuel, maximizing your personal and professional productivity. The author and pulmonology expert, Raj Dasgupta believes "various hormone functions and their release are impacted by sleep or circadian rhythm and vice versa." This includes cortisol, estrogen and progesterone, hunger hormones (like insulin, leptin, and ghrelin), melatonin, thyroid hormones, and growth hormones. "These hormones," the Sleep Center of Middle Tennessee explains, "are responsible for maintaining your bodily functions, including but not limited to hunger, appetite, blood sugar, circadian rhythm, sleep-wake cycle, sexual and cardiovascular function, as well as muscle and tissue repair."

Similarly, some University of Pennsylvania researchers conducted a study where subjects who were constrained to only 4.5 hours of sleep per night for one week reported feeling more stressed, angry, sad, and mentally exhausted. When they reverted to the regular 7–9 hours of sleep, they reported a significant improvement in their moods. By modifying your sleep pattern, you can therefore affect positive changes on your appetite, sexual function, heartbeat, and blood sugar.

According to the National Sleep Foundation, "healthy adults need between 7–9 hours of sleep per night." This allows your body and mind to recharge, leaving you refreshed and alert when you wake up. Getting a whole night's sleep can improve your immune system and mood. Scientific evidence proves that sufficient sleep helps memory and can prevent weight gain. On the flip side, not sleeping enough can affect your alertness, memory, and increase stress. This added to the stress you already experience at work daily will leave you feeling grumpy and irritated. Adopting a good sleeping habit may also reduce your chances of developing heart diseases and diabetes. You do not save time by depriving yourself of sleep; you will on the contrary eventually break down (especially if your work requires creative input). Your efficiency will be compromised, causing you to spend more time completing simple task that would ordinarily be cleared within shorter duration. In addition, it is important to know that inability to sleep may be due to a known or underlying medical condition. If you have difficulties sleeping, I suggest you seek professional help.

## JOURNAL PROMPTS FOR SLEEP

- In one word, describe how you would like your day to go tomorrow. What kind of day would you like to have? What would you like to focus on tomorrow?
- Observe your sleep pattern for a week. Note the time you went to bed, your duration of sleep, and how you feel after waking up. Identify what you ate or drank that may have influenced your sleep. Each morning, ascertain how you are feeling. What can you learn from it? Do you recognize negative patterns you could avoid? This exercise will also help you decipher the ideal hours of sleep your body requires and what facilitates it.

## STRATEGIES FOR SLEEP

- Do a brain dump before going to bed. One hour before bed, write everything on your mind till you cannot think of anything else. Keep the paper where you can find it the next day, but do not think about it anymore.
- Always keep a journal next to your bed. If your mind is still busy after the brain dump, you can continue writing until your mind feels free.
- Avoid heavy meals and eat at least two hours before going to bed.
- Do not consume caffeine at least five hours before bed. A 2013 study published in the "Journal of Clinical Sleep Medicine" indeed reported that consuming caffeine up to six hours before bed can have a harmful effect on your capacity to sleep soundly.
- Renounce drinking for several days per week to ensure you have restful sleep. If you drink, avoid doing it at least 3 hours before bed.
- Increase your daytime natural light exposure and reduce your blue light exposure at night. Blue light is light from electronic devices such as computers, energy-efficient lightbulbs, and smartphones that can negatively alter your circadian rhythm and result in sleep disruption. You can make it a rule to turn off all electronic devices at least one hour before bedtime. During that period, you can take a bath, do some stretches, meal prep for the next day, or read a book.
- Stop the dopamine loop. Adjust the settings on your cellphone and all of your devices so that you do not receive automatic notifications in the evening.

## SET BOUNDARIES

American psychologist, Jacqueline Johnson, says, "Boundaries are a way to take care of ourselves." Setting boundaries is a tactical way to guarantee that you have few close relationships, do not get too involved with others' problems, do not find it difficult to say NO to others' requests, and do not seek to please others for fear of rejection. You need to create boundaries between yourself and other people, and between your work and personal life. If you work from home, you should have a defined space for work. Distinguish your work hours from rest and leisure. Observe yourself more and notice signs such as irritability, and fatigue. These signs remind you that you are crossing your limit.

Creating and adhering to a routine is key to energy management. You can lead a very productive life when you control the energy level you pump into each aspect of your life. You will seamlessly transition from work mode to relaxation, family, or fun mode. All these aspects constitute a fulfilling life. It hurts to realize how many parents are sad and unfulfilled in their old age because they have spent their entire lives away from home, often under the guise of paving way for their children—the same children that will grow to not appreciate or recognize their parental roles due to their persistent absence and negligence. While they thought they were doing the right thing, their children probably spent every day of growing up loathing them for not being present enough.

When you are burning out and your boundaries have been blurred for too long, it is difficult to discern what is good for you from what others think you should do. Reconnecting to your needs can be difficult in these circumstances. Take your time to assess situations before drawing a conclusion or making a decision, to ensure you are doing what is right for you. Auditing your decision (including minor decisions like credit card use, clicking links online and signing up for activities) before executing them can prevent you from falling into crisis. The founder and CEO of

Working Simply, Inc., Carson Tate, has coined a wonderful acronym, **EMPOWER**, for auditing your thoughts and decisions.

E: **Evaluate.** Evaluating the facts is the first step to deciding whether you will take on a project. From the start, ascertain the project's feasibility and duration, alongside your ability to meet up with its demands and deliver an excellent result. You should consider what preparations you need to make and the exact input required of you. Is this in line with your objectives?

M: **My story.** What do you honestly think about the situation? Is it going to be a difficult task or a piece of cake? Are you genuinely willing to take it up, or are you hesitant? What are your true motives for assuming this position? What you need to do here is separate facts from feelings.

P: **Priorities.** What are your priorities? Is the situation in line with what you planned, or is it an outright disruption? Will taking this opportunity impact you negatively in the long run? Is it overly demanding? Be totally honest.

O: **Opportunities.** What do you stand to gain? What is the reward for your sacrifice? Are there financial, professional, mental, or interpersonal gains for you? Every circumstance holds opportunities for the participant. There has to be something in it for you, and you have to identify what that thing is. Is it worth it?

W: **Who.** Who is asking? Is this task of interest to someone who does not mean much to you? Is it your spouse, a superior, or your son? This question can be the dealbreaker. Consider your affiliation with the person who is requesting your input. You may be reluctant to turn down your son's request compared to that of a stranger.

E: **Expectation.** Figure out the internal reasons for your action. Are you genuinely interested in this or are you doing this to prove a point? Are you doing it because it is an emergency? Will this be an opportunity to get better at something? Whose expectations are you meeting—yours or society?

R: **Realistic.** Be realistic and stay true to yourself. Every upside has a downside, which may be obvious or not. Can you handle the downside? Can you incorporate this into your schedule without causing an outright disruption?

## JOURNAL PROMPTS FOR SETTING BOUNDARIES

Healthy boundaries can help you establish healthier, long-lasting relationships. To understand where lines may be blurred, it is necessary to explore the relationships in your life, and ascertain where you need to tighten the boundaries. In addition to your personal interest and wellbeing, your loved ones and your colleagues will also benefit from improved, fulfilling, and healthy relationships.

- When you lack boundaries, you will have difficulty saying NO, and will be overly concerned with the opinion of others. What do you think are the pros and cons of having poor boundaries? Reflect on an aspect of your life where the boundaries are weak and need to be revived.
- Personal boundaries are the limits and rules you set within relationships. Think about three people in your life, and describe the boundaries you have with each one of them. How are they alike, and how are they different?
- Ideally, your boundaries should reflect your values and the things that matter most to you. For example, if you value family time, you might want to set strict boundaries at work to make sure you spend sufficient time with your family. What do you value most, and how do your boundaries reflect these values?
- Influential people in your life act as models and shape the way we set boundaries (both healthy and unhealthy). Think of someone who has helped you

grow and impacted your life greatly. What has this person intentionally or unintentionally taught you about boundaries?

- Do you feel that boundaries are needed in your workplace/relationships? What boundaries could make you feel more comfortable at work/home?
- Are you comfortable sharing your boundaries with others and making your needs known? Do you think you communicate your boundaries effectively? Can you improve the way you communicate your boundaries?
- What boundaries can create the structure/freedom/income/business/life of your dreams? How are you working towards establishing these boundaries?
- What would it feel amazing to say yes to?
- What would it feel liberating to say no to?
- What boundaries no longer serve you? How can you change those boundaries so they start to support you instead?
- What are your working hours? When do you switch off from work? Do you have trouble switching off from work? Why?
- Reflect on the boundaries in all aspects of your life. Where do you have control and where is control lacking?
- Identify the barriers to keeping your boundaries.
- What emotions have you been feeling recently? Are they negative or positive emotions? Do you think you need to balance your emotions better? How can you do this?
- Do you feel like you have enough emotional support? Who is there for you when you need them? Do they offer support you are comfortable with?
- What do you need to grow as a person? Do you have the right people in your life to facilitate your growth? Who can give you the support you need?

- How do you feel when you set a boundary that works for you and has a positive impact on your life?
- What actions can you take to protect your time and energy?

## STRATEGIES FOR SETTING BOUNDARIES

- Learn to say NO. When setting boundaries, there is no need to debate, defend, or over-explain your feelings. Simply be firm, nice, and direct. When faced with resistance, repeat your request or statement. A key element is to stay strong and true to your needs. If you give in, you invite people to disregard your needs.
- Setting boundaries is crucial to establishing your identity. It has the potential to improve your mental health, and well-being. Boundaries can be physical or emotional, and they can be too loose or too rigid. Healthy boundaries often falling somewhere in between. Pay attention when you are low on energy, excited, or feel like crying. Identifying where you need more space, energy and self-respect is the first step to creating healthy boundaries.
- Set a boundary with new commitments: "I appreciate the offer, but I am busy at the moment. I may have to decline. If I get any free time, I'll be sure to inform you."
- Set a boundary to give yourself enough time to consider a request. "Thank you. Please let me think about it and I will come back to you in three days."
- Set a boundary with professional calls in the evening: "I have decided not to answer professional calls when I

am not working to better honor my family's needs. I will call you back as soon as possible on my next working day. Thank you very much for your understanding."

- When setting boundaries, stick to your choice. Do not let yourself be guilted into doing something you feel does not work for you. Be gracious but firm.
- Set boundaries on how long you work, return home and go to bed.
- After journaling on the boundaries you have already established, focus on identifying new boundaries that may be required in your sexual, financial, intellectual, emotional, and physical life, then establish these new boundaries.

## TIME/ENERGY MANAGEMENT

**Manage your time, but manage your energy even more.**

It is surprising that almost every motivational coach will tell you to manage your time by waking up with the sun and heading out early. No one ever says that time is not your most relevant resource —energy is. While this may be arguable, I believe that surplus time does not equate to significant achievements. You may manage your time so well that you have enough time for everything, but if the first two activities you engage in sap every ounce of energy you can muster, you will end up with ample time, but no energy to accomplish more tasks. On the flip side, if you do not have sufficient time, you can make significant impacts with enough energy and enthusiasm. This does not imply that you choose energy at the expense of time or vice versa. I want you to understand that as much as you conserve time, conserve your energy.

Human energy can be likened to water in a bottle. It is regulated and naturally limited. You may have no idea how much you have, but that does not change the fact that your energy is limited. When you spill water from that bottle on plants that will not germinate, you waste your energy, and replenishing the bottle consumes time. Similarly, your daily energy is limited. Regardless of how much time you have, you cannot accomplish a lot if you squander it on unproductive activities or those not directly related to the things that matter. Some people also like to think of human energy as batteries. You will waste them if you power irrelevant things. Afterward, you will have to wait to recharge.

## JOURNAL PROMPTS FOR TIME/ENERGY MANAGEMENT

- Think about the most important things in your life. Isolate yourself from electronics, noise, and similar distractions, so that you are by yourself in a clean environment, relaxed posture, and an uncluttered mind. Evaluate your energy and see where your most important efforts go to. Critically assess your job and personal life to identify aspects that require the most energy input.
- Are you using your time wisely? Where have you invested your energy? Write down your daily activities for two days. Did you check your Facebook? If yes, for how long? Were you distracted while working? How often were you interrupted? After two days, analyze what you wrote. Do you easily get overwhelmed or distracted? Were you able to complete your tasks? How can you make each day more productive?

## STRATEGIES FOR TIME/ENERGY MANAGEMENT

- Pay more attention to yourself by studying when you get tired, bored, or realize your productive rate hits a sharp decline. Do not hesitate to track those moments to find out why you feel this way. If you feel overworked, observe the symptoms that led to the realization. This will help you determine how much you can do before you get tired.
- When you identify how much you can do, ensure you stick to it. Do not exceed your limit unless there is an emergency. Unexpected situations will require you to stress yourself some times, but do not make your entire life an emergency. Understand how much you can handle at any particular time and cultivate the habit of saying NO as you approach your limit. If you have trouble setting limits, consider enrolling for mentorship on setting boundaries.
- Think about how you can implement more time with the people you love into your schedule. Add these moments to your schedule for the week and make sure to fulfill them no matter what.
- Nature has a way of healing. Spend enough time in nature, and remember to slow down to appreciate the moment when you do. This may mean walking in a park, rearing a pet, or simply sitting on a bench to appreciate nature's magic.
- Do not attempt to do everything at the once. Concentrate on what you genuinely love. As opposed to caring about activities you or others *think* you should be doing, focus on what allows you to stay active and care for your mental and physical wellness.

# CHAPTER 9
# ADDRESSING BURNOUT THROUGH RELATIONSHIPS

---

*If civilization is to survive, we must cultivate the science of human relationships- the ability of all peoples, of all kinds, to live together, in the same world at peace.*

FRANKLIN D. ROOSEVELT

---

As social beings, we engage in different types and levels of relationships throughout our lifetime, including friendships, family relationships, acquaintanceships, and romantic relationships. These connections serve as anchors for happiness and fulfillment. At the heart of it, we often need one another, and interpersonal relationships help us navigate our life journeys. From an artistic perspective, "to touch can be to give life," says Michelangelo, the famous Italian sculptor. This position has been further reinforced by several scientific studies. Tiffany Field, a leader in the field of touch, discovered that preterm newborns who received only three 15-minute sessions of touch therapy each day for 5 to 10 days gained 47 percent more weight than premature infants who receive standard medical treatment.

Similarly, studies by Darlene Francis and Michael Meaney

uncovered that rats whose mothers licked and groomed them abundantly when they were infants grow up to be calmer and more resilient to stress, with a stronger immune system.

Dacher Keltner, a social psychologist, says, "Several studies show that touch signals safety and trust, it soothes. Basic warm touch calms cardiovascular stress." He further states that "it activates the body's vagus nerve, which is intimately involved with our compassionate response, and a simple touch can trigger release of oxytocin, the love hormone."

In another study by Jim Coan and Richard Davidson, participants laid in an fMRI brain scanner and were required to anticipate a painful blast of white noise. The scanner revealed that participants experienced heightened brain activity in regions associated with threat and stress, similar to what happens in electrocution as you keenly anticipate what is about to happen. However, participants whose romantic partner stroked their arm while they waited did not show this reaction at all. It was strong evidence that touch had turned off the threat switch. This is a tremendous indication that our social relationships can have huge impacts on our physical and psychological response to situations.

Being surrounded by love is an underrated blessing. A caress from your child, friend, or partner may seem ordinary, but studies have established that these gestures can enormously contribute to our mental and physical wellness; hence, nurturing quality, healthy relationships is vital to your burnout recovery process. It may feel liberating to associate with someone that understands the crease on your forehead, or the happiness in your eyes—someone that shares your worries. They understand your discomfort and are happy to contribute whatever they can to see you back in shape. Their enthusiasm can be so powerful that it leaves you with a feeling of belonging. It makes you feel alive, important, wanted, and inspires your sense of purpose.

A report by Headspace, an Australian counseling association suggests that "we're wired to connect to others from the time we're born. Sometimes, when faced with challenges, we can withdraw from people. But building our connections with people, instead of withdrawing, can change our thoughts and feelings for the better." By extension, we have an emotional obligation to be there for one other, and it must span beyond the good times. Oftentimes, a person suffering burnout may not acknowledge that they need solace and connection. They may reject your offer of support. It is in these moments that you must employ compassion and patience to draw them closer.

In November 2018, Rich Alati who played poker in the US bet US$100,000 that he could survive 30 days alone and in total darkness. He was kept in a little dark room that contained nothing but a bed, fridge, and bathroom. Technically, he had all he needed to survive but he had to negotiate for release after 20 days. He could not survive being alone and he took a payout of US$62,400. Upon release, he explained that hallucination, change in sleep cycle, and awkwardness were key problems he tackled. His experience substantiated the scientific fact that humans are designed to interact by default. Touch, communication, emotional connection, and compliments can have profound effects on our physical and psychological wellness. It also confirmed the research of the psychologist, Kevin Bernett, who observed that most prisoners complained of mental conditions associated with isolation.

From the perspective of the Northwestern Medicine Psychologist and Relationship Expert Sheehan D. Fisher, "It's important to not focus on trying to get everything you need from one relationship. Instead, focus on having a network of social support with a variety of relationships to sustain your well-being and quality of life."

How can your relationship with people help you navigate your burnout? To foster your understanding of this, we will discuss five ways your interpersonal relationships can improve your burnout recovery journey, including journal prompts and strategies to guide your approach toward establishing and nurturing wholesome, sustainable relationships.

## LISTENING EAR AND SOLACE

It is important to have people that genuinely understand you. When life threatens to break you, you need people who can see right through you and come to your aid—to listen and provide a safe space for you to unpack your heart and worries, people who will not judge your psychological meltdowns and insufficiencies resulting from burnout. Empirical studies show that people are more concerned when a familiar person is in a difficult situation compared to when the person is a total stranger, which supports the concept of nurturing healthy relationships wherever you find yourself. Build good relationships with your superiors, peers, and juniors at work. A supportive and transparent working environment can prevent as well as aid recovery from burnout.

Communication can vastly improve your burnout condition and provides relief even when a lasting solution is yet to be established. You may, however, be hesitant to open up or experience psychological dissatisfaction toward expressing yourself for fear of feeling inferior, ridiculed, or problematic. If faced with a such situation, you may not open up until it is too late. You may not have the right words to describe your situation or you may feel stupid talking about it. You may even have the impression your explanations come off as disjointed descriptions and broken stories. Your default instinct would be to handle your frustration by yourself. This is where active listening and communicating skills become vital. An empathetic partner will see through your pain and unspoken worries, and determine how to help you to the best of their knowledge and understanding of you.

On your part, endeavor to be more vocal about your struggles and communicate your expectations to ensure you are not left feeling frustrated. Surround yourself with people that care. It may be tough to trust someone enough to share yourself with them, especially your deepest darkness and vulnerability, but you cannot spend your entire life in distrust. Trust is critical to every healthy relationship. You need to build supportive and positive relationships to recover from burnout and find joy in your life.

## STRATEGIES FOR DEALING WITH CONFRONTATION

- Writing has served as an invaluable therapy for generations. It is especially important for you in the process of mending a relationship with others and yourself. When confrontation arises, begin a resolution procedure by writing down what happened. Highlight your feelings, actions, possible wrongs, and why you think you may be right or wrong. This will clarify your perspective of the situation and your role in it. You must be honest. Bring yourself to admit that mending a relationship is not about being right or wrong. It is about what is at stake.
- If a situation or event bothers you, write a letter. It can be a letter to yourself or to someone else. Read it aloud, so that your brain can accept and welcome your emotions. Process the information, and let it go. Afterward, discard the letter and never think about it again. It has served its purpose.
- If a discussion gets heated, take time to cool off. When you feel more settled and less agitated, all parties involved should participate in a friendly, polite dialogue. The intention here is to share your emotions, thoughts, apologize if necessary, and explain your reaction to foster understanding and establish a common ground. Remember to be honest and openly discuss what may have bothered you.

- When feeling overwhelmed, seek the help of a counselor, mentor, experienced friend, or relative who will understand and guide you.
- Communicate more and criticize constructively.
- Reflect on your most valuable relationships. Why are they so valuable? What values are you looking for in a partner or best friend?
- When faced with a difficult situation, evaluate your role in it. Be intentional about making things work. Is the other party open and equally seeking the same understanding and self-reflection as you are? Do they want to grow and learn from this? Or are they looking for someone to blame?

## SUPPORT

Support can be professional, physical, emotional, or psychological. When you build the right relationship with people, they will be willing to help you stabilize your career as you recover from burnout. Encouraging words can serve as morale boosters and can also empower you to fight self-doubt that may have beclouded your mind.

Changing your routine is the first step in the burnout healing process. You may need to reduce your workload or modify your work habits, and these changes will require external support to reflect any significant improvement. This is another critical way relationships can help your burnout recovery. A good friend can offer to execute some of your tasks. A concerned boss can reduce your workload. You can even get an unpaid mentorship from someone who knows what you are going through.

## CONSTRUCTIVE CRITICISM

When you build relationships with the right people, they can rejuvenate your self-esteem, motivate you, guide you towards your goals, and help improve your life choices. This is particularly true of overachievers and perfectionists. An overachiever or a perfectionist does not know when to draw the line. They may overwork and fret over mistakes. A perfectionist can burnout and adapt poorly to change. Having good company makes it easier. People can tell you when they think you are overworking or advise you to take a break when they notice a decline in your productivity. Your partner can remind you to go to bed, and your supervisor can tell you when you have met the required standard. The fact that they can encourage, support, relieve, mentor, and caution you are critical reasons you should build and maintain relationships with people whether you have already been diagnosed or burnout or not.

## STRATEGIES ON IMPROVING CONNECTION WITH PEOPLE

- Make eye contact when you talk to people.
- Give genuine, positive feedback on other people's efforts.
- Make it a habit to engage physical conversations or calls, rather than texts. You can draw more inferences from bodily gestures and tone.
- Ask open questions and subconsciously think about creative ways to engage people. Tell them what you appreciate about them.
- Avoid putting all the blame on others, when you also have the responsibility of communicating effectively. The burnout recovery process requires open communication and constructive criticism to be effective.

## FEELING OF BELONGING

Have you met someone and wondered where they had been all along? Have you ever found someone so thoughtful and kind that you are certain you could never forget them? Have you met that incredible genius who knows just what to say and how to work their way into your heart? Finding someone that is right for you can be incredibly liberating and valuable. The right partner, the right friend the right boss, the right assistant—people that pay attention to know when you are inconvenienced. They know you inside out and understand what obstacle to knock off your path and what blessings to send your way. It is one thing for someone to say they love you. Watching them express it at times of distress takes it a mile further. Surround yourself with the right people, who understand you and are happy to work with you, and acknowledge when you find yourself in a toxic environment where your physical or mental wellness is trivialized. When you are around the right people, you will feel happier. The burdens you bear will feel light and you will feel as though there is no better place to be.

## A NOTE ON SOCIAL MEDIA

Try to limit your time on social media platforms. While social media is great for networking and bringing people together—especially in COVID and post-COVID times—it fosters connectivity, not intimacy. It will never have the same effect as physical connection and interaction. Social media can have negative effects, especially when your mind is already compromised. It can result in unhealthy comparison, FOMO (Fear of Missing Out), self-doubt, self-criticism, contempt, and poor time management.

# CHAPTER 10
# ADDRESSING BURNOUT THROUGH TIME MANAGEMENT

So far, we have discussed practical methods to approach your burnout condition and regain control of your life. Another key aspect of your burnout recovery journey is time management. Time management involves exercising a variety of skills including prioritizing, goal-setting, scheduling, and strategic thinking. Corporate Finance Institute defines time management as "the process of planning and controlling how much time to spend on specific activities." This definition suggests that time management is about allocating time frames to the different activities you have to engage. It also entails deciding what activities to expend time and energy on, and setting boundaries to ensure you are not deviating, as not every activity will be worth your time. This will have a significant impact on your productivity, coordination, and also help you hit your milestones, which will result in morale boost and fulfillment. You will feel closer to achieving your goals. Adequate time management also means knowing when to rest and relieve yourself of stress. You will learn to prioritize your most important activities and discard those that do not serve any purpose in your life.

Now that you know the benefits of time management, the big question is how exactly can it be infused into your burnout recovery journey? We will now discuss nine practical ways to manage your burnout through time management.

## CREATE A TO-DO LIST

Creating a to-do list will help you focus on what is absolutely necessary. It entails documenting the most important tasks in your life and allocating time for them to be executed. To create a perfect to-do list, begin by listing out every task you have to accomplish. Assign deadlines to each one and identify their importance. Remember to prioritize **urgent and important** tasks over those that are **important but not urgent**. Frequently update your to-do list and tick them off when they are successfully accomplished. Keep it realistic. Unrealistic goals will only result in overexertion and subsequently burnout. Be honest to avoid imposing unnecessary time constraint on yourself. How long will it take you to complete a task in the best possible way? Do not allocate less time, and do not allocate more time than required. Your schedule should be crafted in a way that works for you and not *against* you. The trick is to achieve balance and meet all your goals without exhausting yourself. Here are some useful tips you can use to create an effective to-do list:

1. When you have to deal with a big project, break it down into smaller, less intimidating, and manageable bits. Expand the bullet point; be specific and detailed about the actions required so that it feels more feasible. You will also have more sense of direction and willingness to engage the task.
2. Highlight only 5–7 specific items on your to-do list daily. Ensure they are realistic, include deadlines, and

account for rest. If needed, you can create up to three separate lists: a master list, including all your long-term goals; a weekly list that contains everything you need to do in the next seven days; and the priority to-do list of urgent tasks. Daily scrutiny of your master and weekly list will alert you to any activity that needs to be moved to the priority/urgent list.

3. Allocate estimated time frames to every task on your to-do list. A schedule will help you see more clearly and make sure you don't forget about it. Choose specific times and places to accomplish these tasks.
4. Give time gaps between tasks (15–20 minutes) to accommodate unforeseen situations. It will help you to avoid being trapped by your own schedule.
5. Remember to schedule time for rest. Resting will help you recharge, reenergize, and stay productive. Otherwise, it will be difficult to accomplish your tasks.

To-do lists are great tools for focus, time management, and goal-setting. You will discover how much time you can save by defining and adhering to your schedule. However, do not be hard on yourself if you deviate from your plan sometimes. Your to-do list is devised to facilitate your success, and should not be another source of stress. Do not blame yourself or agonize over uncompleted tasks. You showed up and you did your best. Persevering and trying again the next day is the real accomplishment.

## START EARLY

Starting early is key to ticking off every task on your list as well as retiring in good time. Medical doctor, Raj Dasgupta, says, "Studies at the National Institute of Health suggests that people who wake up early tend to go to bed earlier and enjoy longer, better quality sleep. Alongside, starting early allows more time to carry out the activities on your list." Waking up early will help you afford personal time to plan and strategize before starting the day. It will also help you stay organized, beat the wild traffic, and gain more control of your life. When you start early, you have enough time to execute activities that improve your positivity and energy throughout the day, such as meditation, work out, or yoga. In the most practical sense, starting early creates more you-time and undisturbed relaxation.

As part of your effort to make the best of every morning, limit your time on social media and avoid falling into the trap of starting your morning with work—checking your inbox, for example. This is *your* time. As I now always say, there is absolutely nothing that cannot wait until 9 a.m. The world will not end if an email is not read before then.

Adopting the habit of getting up early is great, but you should not criticize yourself when you do not have the energy to meet up with your expectations and schedule. I recall a time in my life when I was desperate to integrate waking up early into my routine, so desperate that I was not flexible about it. I became irritable and stressed when I was not in bed before midnight—ending up too stressed to fall asleep. Then I would get angry at myself for not waking up early in the morning and criticize myself for ruining my day.

If you do not wake up as early as you had hoped, rather than leaving the house in a lousy mood, accept the situation. Smile through it. The sooner you ditch the black-and-white mentality, the better. Life unfolds in a way that accommodates grey areas. It will not always go as planned, but you can always do your best regardless of life's uncertain nature. Assure yourself that you will try again tomorrow.

If the main cause is related to a sleep disorder, you could evaluate yourself to know if there are underlying reasons you always wake up late and are reluctant to work. Then plan how to address the situation.

## FOCUS AND PRIORITIZE YOUR TASKS

It is important to give every activity on your to-do list its fair share of required attention to obtain the best results. Knock off one task and move to the next. It may not be easy especially if you struggle with maintaining attention for long durations. Colleagues, emails, calls, and reunions may prevent you from working effectively for an extended duration. You may get distracted and check social media. Or get lost staring outside the window, observing the outfit of pedestrians and the color of vehicles. This may be the consequence of having spent too much time without taking a break from work. You may also be distracted by your own wandering thoughts. Do not beat yourself up. Notice your attention wander and gently nudge yourself back on track. Self-compassion is key as we have discussed earlier.

Focusing means channeling your physical/mental energy into resolving it a particular task at a given time. This does not mean you overly prioritize the task. You only need to ensure that within the stipulated time for it, you focus on it and avoid distractions. Soledad Ballesteros, a Spanish experimenter and professor of Basic Psychology reported that the presence of distracting information captures attention and impairs the mind's ability to concentrate. It can cost between 23 minutes and 15 seconds to get back on track. "Also," says Sarah Robertson, "when we are 'checking our inbox' we are often in a mode of thinking that is distracted and on autopilot, driven by a need for a dopamine hit. Dopamine is a chemical released into the brain that gives a flash of feel-good-factor. We get a dopamine hit when we check our email; it's the feeling of release from the anxiety of 'I've not checked my emails recently.' We also get a dopamine hit when we close the loop on something; we get the email that answers our question, the loop gets closed, and we feel good." It is not surprising that we constantly want to check our messages, emails, and social networks throughout the day. We are simply addicted to this dopamine rush.

## STRATEGIES TO IMPROVE YOUR FOCUS

- Try turning your email notifications off and only check your inbox at specific times of the day. You could check once in the morning and once in the afternoon. Having self-control will improve your focus and productivity.
- Keep a list of your accomplishments so far or a "done" list from the previous day. Celebrating the small victories will give you motivation to undertake greater challenges.
- You can multitask but do not multi-focus. A good example of multitasking is running the printing machine while looking through another document on your desktop screen. Only one of those tasks requires your active attention. Multi-focusing, on the other hand, implies you are engaging in two activities that require your attention; like answering emails and working on a business presentation for example. This will diminish your efficiency and productivity.
- To ensure you do not multi-focus, make a list of activities that require focus and those that do not. That way, you can easily integrate activities and multitask.
- If you are feeling overwhelmed, brain dump all your thoughts and ideas on paper. This will relieve your mind and help your brain focus on more important activities. Those activities that are not overly important and can be postponed will be put aside for the moment.

## DECLUTTER YOUR SPACE AND BRAIN

Keeping an uncluttered mental and physical environment is vital to focus. A desk covered with all sorts of files, a tie laying carelessly at the corner, cups of coffee sitting among stacks of documents and patiently waiting to spill, a computer at a corner with several tabs open—all these put together will create the perfect chaos and recipe for confusion, irritation, and exhaustion. With too many things on your desk, it may seem like you have too much to do, whereas things are simply disorganized. When you tuck them away neatly, you may realize that you were not as overwhelmed as you thought. Keep only documents that are currently under review on your desk. Do away with the coffee mug as soon as you are done with it. Organize your files into separate sections as needed and close tabs that you do not need.

Similarly, pay attention to your thoughts. Notice when it is roaming and drifting away. Notice when your attention is fading and digressing toward something of minimal importance. If you feel overwhelmed, take a break to clear your mind. A cluttered mind is as chaotic as a cluttered desk, although way less obvious to the eye. Consciousness is the ultimate tool to tidy your mind and stay focused.

## FIX PERSONAL DEADLINES

Underestimating personal deadlines is one of the biggest mistakes I made while working as an accountant. I knew the task at hand, and I could safely estimate how long it would take to complete it, but I rarely did. I preferred to stick to the deadline given to me by the company, which unfortunately never worked. Sometimes, the deadlines set for you by your superior may be unrealistic. You may need more time to complete the task without overexerting yourself. If you feel a work deadline is unreasonable, consider renegotiating terms with your superior. Assure them that you are currently engaging in the task and are doing your best to bring it to fruition. Ask them what tasks they would rather have you prioritize, considering you cannot do them all at the same time. When asked how long you will need to complete a task, be sincere and reasonable with your response. Set close deadlines to avoid procrastinating—but not too close that it is insufficient.

## DELEGATE TASKS

This advice will come in handy if you are a perfectionist or an overachiever. We have earlier agreed that there is nothing wrong with yearning for perfection; the problem is that most times, perfection is a mirage. Great inventors and world-renowned personalities have unanimously agreed that perfection is too unreal to be true. Instead of striving to complete tasks by yourself for fear of others not doing it the exact way you consider appropriate, train the people around you to handle tasks and help them get better every day. Compensate them when they are on track, and find creative ways to demand more without overexerting them. Delegate the less important tasks to people and focus on more important ones to reduce your workload, save time, increase the quality of your delivery, and reduce your chances of burning out.

Delegation and outsourcing are tricky, but this does not change the fact that they are a crucial aspect of the modern workplace. It may be difficult to let someone else complete certain tasks, but remember, you have limited time to complete these tasks and delegating/outsourcing can be a real time-saver. You only have to ensure that you hand over responsibilities to the right person with the required skills to execute them. With this, you can rest easy and not fret over the quality of delivery.

## REDEFINE SUCCESS

Just like comfort and happiness, success is personal—it should be personal. I say 'should be' because oftentimes, we let society or other individuals define what success means to us. Your source of peace may not be my source of peace. What brings me fulfillment may seem very mundane to you. Society has taught us to ascribe success to status, money, or other related items that can be acquired with money. We often forget that we are so different in our thoughts, values, perspectives and backgrounds.

A person who grows up in a family-oriented environment may consider raising a happy, wholesome family a huge accomplishment. A beginner at the gym may consider 20 reps of pushups a significant milestone, whereas a veteran may be aiming for something higher; perhaps 50 or more. As a beginner, if you make a veteran your standard and basis for evaluating your success/progress, you are creating unrealistic standards for yourself and measuring your value on an unfair scale that does not account for your current stage of life. It is great to have role models, but you must understand that they were not always at the level you see them now, the level that makes you admire them; they got there with time and effort. All you have is time and the choice to put in the effort today. What you do today will go a long way in defining where you will be tomorrow. You only have to make it count.

From now on, you must look inward and determine what success looks like for you. Does it mean being happy with your family, having enough to eat, or having a roof over your head? What makes you happy? These questions are personal. To answer these questions, you can meditate and ascertain how you can incorporate your answers into your burnout management process as practical actions.

## EXPLORE DIGITAL TOOLS

Technology resources and digital tools make it easier to manage your time, activities, and boundaries, making your time management strategy more exciting. You have alarms, timers, and time-tracking software at your disposal. You can use various mobile software and desktop applications to set a break reminder. With these in place, you can tell when it is time to unplug for a few minutes and relax. You can set an alarm to remind you when the time allocated to a task is over. You can also journal on your mobile through applications like Trello. Applications like Offtime, Cold Turkey, and Flipd can restrict your access to social media platforms within a specified time and limit distraction. With these aids, your burnout recovery journey does not need to be stressful or overbearing. You have all the tools and resources required to make it work.

## LEARN TO SAY NO

"Many people agree to things—even things they would prefer not to do—simply to avoid the considerable discomfort of saying NO," Dr. Vanessa Bohns, a renowned social psychologist, explains. Saying NO is one of the most difficult things for kind-hearted and diligent people. Naturally, some people worry that it would be disrespectful to turn down offers from others. At other times, we feel empathy for others and get boxed into overwhelming responsibilities alongside what we already have. The implication is that we get overburdened and gradually burn out. To avert such situations, we must learn to say no.

You can be gracious while being unequivocal about your NO. Sometimes, you do not even need to provide a reason at all. You can simply say, "I'm sorry, I can't." You can also consider offering an alternative if and only if you have one. It is not compulsory, so do not inconvenience yourself trying to figure out the other person's problem. If you are still unsure how to say no without betraying yourself, consider seeking mentorship from people around you who have learned to constructively say NO. The first rule of saying no is that it must express kindness. Reinforce your rejection with a potential future collaboration. You can say, "I'm sorry, but I have to pass. I appreciate your thinking of me in this situation. Maybe the next?" You can add some explanation without getting verbose: "I'm sorry, I have other obligations I must attend to this evening. I can't cover for you at work today, but I could help out another time though."

## JOURNAL PROMPTS FOR SAYING NO CONSTRUCTIVELY

- Think about the many times you have been asked for something and notice your common replies. Do you often say yes to everything, while suffering the consequence later? Do you compromise your plans to please others?
- Imagine that you have to turn down an extra project at work. What are the first reactions that come to your mind? What would you say to your colleague or boss? Do you fidget at the thought of it?
- When faced with a difficult situation, ask yourself the following questions to decide whether or not saying "yes" is a good option: Will saying yes prevent me from focusing on something that is more important to me? Does this offer/opportunity/activity align with my values and goals? Would saying yes make me feel even more tired or burned out? Would saying yes be good for my mental health? Or would it worsen my situation?

Saying NO is a great form of self-care. It allows you to create more opportunities to rest and recharge. By saying NO when you need to, you are building a more meaningful life on your own terms, while spending more of your time and energy on things that have the potential to improve the quality of your life. Saying NO may seem difficult at first, but the more you do it, the easier it becomes

—the more natural it will feel. Try not to say yes simply because you want to avoid feeling uncomfortable and guilty. You are not selfish for saying NO. You are only doing what is best for you. Consider whether saying yes is what you really need at the moment before you blurt an 'of course, I'll be glad to help!'

# CONCLUSION

Congratulations on making it this far. You made the bold move to pick up this book and here you are, down to the last page, equipped with new knowledge to forge ahead on your burnout recovery journey. How do you feel? While I may not be able to hear the answer you have whispered in your heart, I hope you do not feel too tired as you read these words—and if you do, that is fine, too. We are all only human after all.

We are all different people with our respective dreams, ambitions, and responsibilities. Every morning, we get out of bed and go again for a reason. Some of these reasons are bound to be excruciating yet challenging to quit, edging you to the point of stress and burnout, and leaving you with nothing but a joyless, unfulfilled life. I have been there, and I know how meaningless life seemed to me while I burned out. It was tormenting.

If you are feeling overwhelmed, on the verge of burnout, or currently burning out, I hope you found the right tools to help you through your journey in the pages of this book; I hope you found some encouragement and solace, some assurance that you are doing your best, you are a work in progress, and you can triumph over this situation that burdens your heart and even much more. If you are simply looking to prevent the occurrence of burnout, I hope you found this book helpful as well.

I wrote this book to share the knowledge that saved me while I wallowed in a dark place when I struggled to find myself but realized I could not recognize the person in the mirror until I decided to fight back and regain control over my life. I am writing this book today because I won, and I want you to know that you can win too, and you will win. Amidst this blurry, tormenting, largely uncertain, and burnout-ridden moment, there is hope. Beyond this place, there is redemption for you. Life can get better than this. You can be happier than this. Focus on where you want to be and keep making the hard choices every day by showing up and doing the work. Little changes are better than nothing and will amount to a huge difference in your life.

Remember, choose what works for you and leave the rest. You do not need to implement everything right away. The aim of this book is to make your life easier and not increase your stress. I genuinely hope you found something that works for you as you journeyed through these pages. I am thrilled and excited about what your future holds, and I would absolutely love to hear about your progress. If you would like to share your progress and parts of this book you find particularly valuable, please leave your comments on the Amazon page. My family and I will be eagerly waiting to read your comments. Until then, I wish you a life filled with adventure, laughter, and bliss.

Best,

*Amber Pierce*

Customer reviews
5 out of 5
4 global ratings

| | | |
|---|---|---|
| 5 star | | 100% |
| 4 star | | 0% |
| 3 star | | 0% |
| 2 star | | 0% |
| 1 star | | 0% |

How customer reviews and ratings work

Review this product
Share your thoughts with other customers

Write a customer review

Leave

A 1-CLICK REVIEW

I WOULD BE INCREDIBLY THANKFUL IF YOU COULD TAKE JUST 60 SECONDS TO WRITE A BRIEF REVIEW ON AMAZON, EVEN IF IT'S JUST A FEW SENTENCES!

BURNOUT RECOVERY

*15 techniques to overcome chronic stress, regain control, restore your energy and your focus*

AMBER PIERCE

## ABOUT THE AUTHOR

Amber Pierce is a writer and financial consultant based in New York. She has been helping people prevent and recover from burnout for over three years, especially through her writings. Having experienced severe burnout firsthand, she knows how difficult it can be to bounce back from a place of hopelessness when you feel trapped and have no energy left for the simplest things.

The professional world is constantly evolving at a fast pace, but business owners, managers, and leaders do not seem to be keeping up. For the individual, it may be challenging to cope with work and personal life while maintaining emotional and mental balance, and general wellbeing. Doing all of these spontaneously may seem terrifying and is often not a smooth sail.

Amber Pierce hopes to guide others on a journey to overcoming the shackles of burnout and emerge into a life of happiness, fulfillment and wellness. She wants to tell you the things she was not told when she first experienced burnout, the things she had to learn along the way through lots of research and experience.

In her free time, Amber likes working out, writing about burnout, and spending as much time as possible with her family. She lives in Seattle with her husband Paul, and son Matthew.

# TWO SPECIAL GIFTS FOR OUR READERS

As a special thank you for getting this book, we would like to give you:

**6 TOOLS & EXERCISES TO OVERCOME STRESS**

Everything you need to help you manage stress in a healthy and effective way

\+

**7-DAY CHALLENGE TO BURNOUT RECOVERY**

A step-by-step guide to kickstart you recovery journey

VISIT THEBURNOUTRECOVERYCLUB.COM/FREE-GIFTS | OR SCAN ME

**TO GET YOURS!**

# REFERENCES

1. Sandee, L. (2022, March 18) Sleep myths that may be keeping you from a good night's rest.CNN.https://www.google.com/amp/s/amp.cnn.com/cnn/2022/03/18/health/sleep-myths-wellness/index.html
2. World Health Organization. (2019) Burn-out an "occupational phenomenon": International Classification of Diseases Burn-out an "occupational phenomenon": International Classification of Diseases
3. Jennifer, M. (2019, December 11) Burnout Is About Your Workplace, Not Your People. Harvard Business Review. Burnout Is About Your Workplace, Not Your People
4. Byung, C. Start Reading The Burnout Society.. Stanford University Press. Start reading The Burnout Society | Byung-Chul Han
5. Sarita, R. (2019, January 7) What are the effects of total isolation? An expert explains. Econotimes. What are the effects of total isolation? An expert explains - EconoTimes
6. Jonathan Malesic, (2022, January 1)The History of Burnout, From the 1970s to the Great Resignation. Washington Post. The history of burnout, from the 1970s to the Great Resignation - The Washington Post
7. Northwestern Medicine University. (2021, September) % Benefits of Healthy Relationships 5 Benefits of Healthy Relationships | Northwestern Medicine
8. Nikita, T. (2021, December 1) What is Burnout, and How Can You Manage It? George Mason University. https://www.gmu.edu/news/2022-02/what-burnout-and-how-can-you-manage-it
9. Blog: why are relationships important?
10. Juli, F. (2019,May 18) A Guide to Burnout. Healthline. How to Identify and Prevent Burnout
11. Maslach, C., & Leiter, M. P. (2016). Understanding the burnout experience: recent research and its implications for psychiatry. *World psychiatry : official journal of the World Psychiatric Association (WPA)*,

15(2), 103–111. Understanding the burnout experience: recent research and its implications for psychiatry - Maslach - 2016

12. Eva, S. (2020, March 6) Nutritional psychiatry: Your brain on food. Harvard Health Publishing. Nutritional psychiatry: Your brain on food - Harvard Health.
13. Alexandra, M. (2016, January 29) Burnout And The Brain. Association for Psychological Science https://www.google.com/url?sa=t&source=web&rct=j&url=https://www.psychologicalscience.org/observer/burnout-and-the-brain&ved=2ahUKEwjq2OWd9vz3AhWygVwKHbMtBt8QFnoECDEQAQ&usg=AOvVaw1zz_dQ1Dw9O5gMGUvqGA4t
14. Harvard Health Publishing. (2019, April). The gut-brain connection - Harvard Health.
15. North Dakpta Professional Health (2022) Telltale Signs of Physician Burnout | NDPHP | North Dakota Professional Health Program
16. Marnie, V. (2021, September 1) How Sleep Can Affect Your Hormone Levels, Plus 12 Ways to Sleep Deep. Healthline. Missing Sleep? Why Your Hormones May Be Responsible
17. Maria Cohut. (2019, August 2) Burnout: Facing the damage of 'chronic workplace stress. Medical News Today. What is burnout, and how can you cope with it?
18. Jacquelyn, J. (2021, June 2) 10 Ways to Build and Preserve Better Boundaries. PsychCentral 10 Ways to Build and Preserve Better Boundaries I Psych Central
19. Zaria, G. (2019, June 11) How to tell if you're close to burning out. BBC.How to tell if you're close to burning out - BBC Worklife
20. Aron, A., Fisher, H., Mashek, D.J., Strong, G., Li, H., Brown, L.L. (2005). Reward, motivation, and emotion systems associated with early-stage intense romantic love. Journal of Neurophysiology, 94, 327–337. Google Scholar | Crossref | Medline | ISI
21. Mora, L. (2021, November 8) Burnout: How to Avoid It, How to Know When You're Burned Out, and What to Do About It. Everyday Health. https://www.everydayhealth.com/burnout/
22. Alexandra, V. (2020, October 20) Number Of People Reporting Anxiety And Depression Nationwide Since Start Of Pandemic Hits

All-Time High In September, Hitting Young People Hardest. Mental Health America. Number of people reporting anxiety and depression nationwide since start of pandemic hits all-time high in September, hitting young people hardest | Mental Health America

23. Dr. Heather J. Moday, MD | Philadelphia, PA | Internist | US News Doctors
24. National Library of Medicine (2020, June) https://www.ncbi.nlm.nih.gov/books/NBK279286/#_NBK279286_pubdet_
25. Emma, R. (2020, May 15) The Myth About External Validation. Evoke Therapy. The Myth About External Validation
26. MedlinePlu (2020) Overcoming job stress: MedlinePlus Medical Encyclopedia
27. MedlinePlus [Internet]. Bethesda (MD): National Library of Medicine (US); [updated 2020 Jun 24]. Heart attack; [updated 2020 Jun 10; reviewed 2016 Aug 25; cited 2020 Jul 1]; [about 5 p.]. Available from: https://medlineplus.gov/ency/patientinstructions/000884.htm
28. Kathrynm I. (2021, June 15) Importance of Taking A Vacation. Importance of taking a vacation
29. SummaHealth (2021) Stress Management: How to tell the difference between Good and Bad Stress. Stress Management: The Difference Between Good & Bad Stress | Summa Health
30. Stacey, L. (2020, December 20) Why You're Still Tired. Dr. Saundra Dalton Smith On The Severn Types of Rest We All Need. Maria Shriver. Why You're Still Tired: Dr. Saundra Dalton-Smith on the 7 Types of Rest We All Need | Stacey Lindsay
31. Kenda, C. (2019, August 18) How The Fight or Flight Response Works.VeryWellMind How the Fight-or-Flight Response Works
32. Elizabeth, S.(2020, June 28) When Stress is Actually Good For You https://www.verywellmind.com/what-kind-of-stress-is-good-for-you-3145055
33. Merriam Webster Online Dictionary (2022, June) Brain fog Definition & Meaning - Merriam-Webster
34. Speaker Spotlight (2021, July) Productivity Expert Chris Bailey Shares Six Burnout Triggers To Watch Out For. Chris Bailey on the Six Triggers that Lead to Burnout

35. Dietrich Bonhoeffer Quotes. (n.d.). BrainyQuote.com. Retrieved June 9, 2022, from BrainyQuote.com Web site: Dietrich Bonhoeffer - The essence of optimism is that it...
36. Karin, G. (2-22, March 31) How to Treat and Prevent Mental Exhaustion. Healthline. Mental Exhaustion: Definition, Causes, Symptoms, and Treatment, http://www.yeoh.com/pict_files/IADIS%20Conference%20final%208.pdf
37. Fagerlind Ståhl, AC., Ståhl, C. & Smith, P. Longitudinal association between psychological demands and burnout for employees experiencing a high versus a low degree of job resources. *BMC Public Health* 18, 915 (2018). Longitudinal association between psychological demands and burnout for employees experiencing a high versus a low degree of job resources | BMC Public Health
38. Christine,H. (2020, March 3) Finding New Ways To Rest Finding New Ways to Rest — Christine Hoover, MA, LPC
39. Natalie, C. (2017, February 24) Why Motivation is Important In Life. Why Motivation is Important in Life
40. Ranbir Kapoor Quotes. (n.d.). BrainyQuote.com. Retrieved June 9, 2022, from BrainyQuote.com Web site: Ranbir Kapoor - I believe that working with good people...
41. Jennifer, K. (2022) The mind is its own place and, in itself can make a heaven of hell or a hell of heaven. The mind is its own place and, in itself can make a heaven of hell or a hell of heaven." - John Milton - Nimble Quotes
42. Gragnano, A., Simbula, S., & Miglioretti, M. (2020). Work-Life Balance: Weighing the Importance of Work-Family and Work-Health Balance. *International journal of environmental research and public health*, *17*(3), 907. Work–Life Balance: Weighing the Importance of Work–Family and Work–Health Balance
43. Melinda, S. (2021,October) Narcissistic Personality Disorder. HelpGuide. https://www.helpguide.org/articles/mental-disorders/narcissistic-personality-disorder.html
44. Maslach, C., & Leiter, M. P. (2016). Understanding the burnout experience: recent research and its implications for psychiatry. *World psychiatry : official journal of the World Psychiatric Association (WPA)*,

15(2), 103–111. Understanding the burnout experience: recent research and its implications for psychiatry - Maslach - 2016

45. Skipping Stones. (March, 2020). Finding Sensory Rest https://www.goskippingstones.com/blog/sensory-rest
46. The Jarkata Post. (July, 2018). 10-minute rests can improve memory, says study http://www.thejakartapost.com/life/2018/07/08/10-minute-rests-can-improve-memory-says-study.html
47. Healthline. (February, 2019). Licensed Psychologist, Juli Fraga shares How Living In a City Can Mess With Your Mental Health. https://www.healthline.com/health/mental-health/living-in-a-city
48. Amy Isler, RN, MSN. (May, 2021). How Can I Tell If I'm Experiencing Burnout or Depression? https://www.goodrx.com/well-being/healthy-mind/depression-vs-burnout
49. Ivan Ramirez. (September, 2018). On Values and Work Burnout. https://medium.com/@ivaramme/on-values-and-work-burnout-2fa2839c6d63
50. Emily Morse. (May, 2022). Relationship Burnout Causes: How to Recover Your relationship. Masterclass Articles. https://www.masterclass.com/articles/relationship-burnout#what-is-relationship-burnout
51. Kimberly Zapata. (October, 2021). Dear Exhausted and Burnt-Out Parents, We're Here to Help. https://www.healthline.com/health/parenting/parental-burnout
52. Social Market Foundation. (October, 2015). Happiness and productivity: Understanding the happy-productive worker. *Global Perspective Series: Paper* http://www.smf.co.uk/wp-content/uploads/2015/10/Social-Market-Foundation-Publication-Briefing-CAGE-4-Are-happy-workers-more-productive-281015.pdf#page=9